agriculturalist

THE NEW PHYSICS

The New Physics

Talks on Aspects of Science

by

SIR C. V. RAMAN

PHILOSOPHICAL LIBRARY

New York

PRINTED IN THE UNITED STATES OF AMERICA

INTRODUCTION

It is a truism to remark that within the last few years physics has assumed an overwhelming importance to the layman. The development of atomic (or rather nuclear) energy is a single obvious example of this trend. Yet to the great majority physics remains the most mysterious of all the sciences. It has often been said that although ninety-nine out of a hundred people, when questioned, will cite Einstein as the greatest living scientist, very few of those ninety-nine will have any but the vaguest concept of the actual contributions of Einstein to scientific progress. This is an unhealthy situation, for even in this age of specialization it is essential that people have some acquaintance with a science which has affected and will continue to affect their lives to such a great extent.

"The New Physics" is therefore motivated by a real need. It was originally delivered as a series of radio talks to the Indian public, and hence is primarily intended for the layman. Professor Raman, India's most distinguished physicist, has discussed those parts of nature with which all of us come into contact, but which few of us attempt to understand: water, soil, weather, atmospheric electricity, the structure of crystals, and other topics. Although the study of these subjects will of course not lead to an understanding of such subjects as the theory of relativity, it is a first step in the right direction.

Furthermore these matters are of interest in their own right. Physics as a rule has been able to make progress only by idealizing nature and treating such simple systems as bodies falling through a vacuum. Clearly real events in nature, such as those discussed in this book, are infinitely more complicated, and hence their exact treatment presents great difficulties.

On the other hand the discussion of familiar events in nature is desirable in a book of this kind, since thereby the non-specialist may see everyday phenomena illuminated from a new point of view and in this way gain some insight into the methods of modern science.

Sir Chandrashekhar Venkat Raman, the author of "The New Physics," is well qualified to discuss this subject. Founder of the Indian Academy of Sciences, co-founder of the Indian Journal of Physics, and indeed the guiding spirit in the current growth of physics in India, he was in 1930 the recipient of the Nobel Prize in Physics for his discovery of the effect which bears his name, one of the important experiments of the preceding decade.

Raman found that light scattered by certain substances may have a slightly changed color from the original light beam. This effect is hard to account for according to nineteenth century physics, whereas it may be definitely predicted on the basis of the new quantum theory, of which it is therefore an important experimental confirmation. Furthermore, the Raman effect makes it possible to investigate, by means of visible and ultra-violet light, details of molecular and atomic structure which would otherwise be measurable only by infra-red light, which presents great experimental difficulties. In this way many interesting properties of atoms and molecules have been discovered.

In fact, it has even been possible to use the Raman effect to gain information concerning atomic nuclei. Needless to say, this is of great interest to physicists today, since so little is known about nuclear structure.

Physics by its very nature requires extreme specialization on the part of its students. Its conclusions, which must eventually predict numbers for the results of actual measurements, are best expressed in mathematical formulae. This has the disadvantage of making the subject well-nigh unintelligible to the layman. There are unfortunately few teachers who are able to surmount this handicap. Professor Raman has written a book which avoids this pitfall and thus should give the lay reader an opportunity of penetrating at least part of the way into the mysteries of this interesting and important science.

FRANCIS LOW

Institute for Advanced Study
Princeton, N. J.

TABLE OF CONTENTS

THE NEW PHYSICS

Chapter I

THE NEW PHYSICS

AN IRISHMAN, if there be one amongst my listeners to-night, might feel inclined to ask me the question, how old is this New Physics about which you are talking to us? My answer would be—exactly forty-three years old and still going strong. The world heard the new baby crying when it was born—I am referring to the enormous excitement created by the announcement of a German physicist, Rontgen, that he had discovered a new kind of radiation with amazing properties, which we now call by his name, or alternatively "X-rays." This experimental discovery by Rontgen had far-reaching effects. It opened the eyes of men of science to the fact that the courageous and patient investigator could hope to discover new phenomena in Nature undreamt of in the natural philosophy of the nineteenth century. Rontgen's discovery, in fact, was the beginning of the new physics. The stimulus to novel types of experimentation which it gave resulted in a whole new crop of discoveries, many of which in their intrinsic interest and importance are not surpassed even by Rontgen's own magnificent finding. During the past four decades, the spate of new phenomena has flowed into physics with undiminished vigour, so much so that it is becoming increasingly difficult even for a man of science—excepting, of course, the discoverer himself, to feel thrilled by a new physical phenomenon.

I will not fatigue you by a recital of the names of even the most outstanding investigators who have built up the physics of today. Their names and their discoveries are known to every student of physics. They are claimed as nationals by one or another of many different countries. Yet in the truest sense they belong to the whole world and to the international brotherhood of science. I will permit myself to mention only two of the greatest pioneers. Amongst the priceless memories that a man of science like myself treasures life-long is that of personal contact with such leaders of science as the late Lord Rutherford and the late Madame Curie; their contributions to the building of the new physics have been most impressive, and their influence on their generation and on the progress of science almost incredibly great.

I would not be fair either to my listeners or to my subject if I conveyed the impression that the new physics has been built up entirely by the work of experimenters. This is far from being the case. Indeed the amazing progress of the new physics has been due to no small extent to the courageous leadership and constant guidance given to experimenters by the theoretical physicists or natural philosophers, who in turn build on the foundations firmly laid by experi-

mental discovery. I do not believe there is a single lis-
tener to my talk who has not heard of Einstein and his
relativistic philosophy which forms an integral part of
the framework of thought in the new physics. Not
all my listeners, however, will have heard of Professor
Niels Bohr of Copenhagen, whose picture hangs facing
that of Lord Rutherford at the head of the staircase
in my house at Bangalore. Prof. Bohr, as he often re-
minds his listeners, comes from one of the smallest
countries in Europe, namely Denmark. But, in the
view of many including myself, he is the greatest natural philosopher of the day. The work of Niels Bohr in
building up a theory of atomic structure which has inspired a host of experimenters in their work is one of
the greatest triumphs of the human mind. In the still
unsolved problems presented by the facts of atomic
disintegration and transmutation, he as the foremost
thinker of the day may yet lead us to a completer understanding of the experimental results.

You may well ask, what has the new physics
achieved? One has only to look back to the physics of
my college days at Madras thirty years ago and to
look at the physics of to-day to appreciate the difference. The old physics was successful chiefly in giving
what might be called a macroscopic or large-scale description of natural phenomena, that is to say, a statement of observed facts regarding the properties of
matter, heat, light, sound, electricity and magnetism.
On the other hand, its attempts to interpret the ob-

served facts in terms of atomistic and molecular concepts was definitely a failure, except in a severely
restricted field. The reason for this failure was that
the old physics had practically no foundation on which
to build. This foundation has been supplied by the discovery of the ultimate sub-atomic units constituting
matter and the laws of their inter-action. The detailed
explanation of all physical phenomena and of the
physical properties of matter has in consequence become a practical proposition. A very great measure of
success has been achieved in this respect in every one
of the recognized divisions of the older physics. Whole
new territories of phenomena not contemplated by the
older physics have also been opened up and brought
under the rule of the new physics.

Not content with these triumphs, the new physics
has entered the field of chemistry and has brought to
find an explanation in terms of sub-atomic processes
for the well-ascertained facts of chemistry regarding
the reactions of atoms with each other to form molecules. Such a task could scarcely be considered super-
fluous. For one of the essential facts of chemistry is
that the strength of chemical combination and the
energy required for or released by such combination is
very different in different cases, and it is only in physical theories that it is possible to find any real understanding of these facts, and indeed also of the real
nature of chemical combination. The success of the
new science known as "chemical physics" has tran-

scended all expectations. Indeed, it is not unreasonable to hope that before many years pass, theoretical chemistry will come to be regarded as a branch of mathematics.

What has been the secret of all these amazing successes? Simply stated, it is the elimination of the Newtonian mechanical laws from the field of atomic and molecular physics and their substitution by other and new laws governing sub-atomic processes. It would take me too long to go deeply into the theoretical aspects of the new physics. It must suffice here to say that they involve a revolutionary change in our outlook regarding natural phenomena and their explanation. The present generation has not yet had time to fully understand and absorb the new theoretical outlook; but the latter has abundantly justified itself by its success in handling problems of the most varied nature. To the next generation, the new modes of thinking now required in our science will doubtless become quite habitual.

I must not neglect to make at least a brief mention of the most recent spectacular triumphs of the new physics, namely the creation of new chemical elements by artificial transmutation of known elements. Lord Rutherford's last little book *The Newer Alchemy* gives a very clear and fascinating account of this newest physics. These remarkable advances described therein were not due to any accidental discovery but were the natural result of the intensive study of the atom and of its structure which is characteristic of the new physics. The chemical identity of an element is determined by the nucleus of the atom, that is by the very small and dense core of the atom. By bombarding the atom with other swift atomic projectiles, transformations may be induced. In many cases the new elements produced are radio-active, in other words they give off electric particles and spontaneously transform themselves into other elements in the manner of the naturally radio-active elements.

For the production of the swift atomic projectiles used in the new syntheses of the chemical elements, amazing new types of apparatus have been developed in which figure gigantic electro-magnets or electro-static generators or electric transformers. By means of special ingenious devices, these are used to speed up the atomic projectiles to very high velocities corresponding to several millions of volts. On the occasion of my visit to the Paris International Conference of Science last year, and in my subsequent tour, I was privileged to see several of these installations in operation. In their boldness and novelty of conception, and in the purposes for which these are used, these contrivances fittingly represent the spirit of the new physics.

The vast body of new knowledge which the new physics has created naturally represents a greatly increased power to use the forces of nature for good and evil. In a hundred different ways, physics has during this period of advance influenced human life and activity. But I would not have you forget that the greatest leaders of our science have always been those whose aim has been the promotion of knowledge for its own sake.

CHAPTER II

PHYSICS IN THE NEWS

THE PURPOSE of scientific study and research is to obtain an ever deeper understanding of the workings of nature. To the physicist falls the task of discovering the ultimate units or entities that constitute the material universe and of ascertaining the principles which govern their behaviour. This quest takes the physicist farther and farther every year, and the end is not yet in sight. The wealth of knowledge gathered on the way has however been immense. It is not hoarded in a treasure chest like a miser's money but given freely away to all who will take it. The discoveries and inventions of the physicist become the working tools of the engineer, the chemist and the biologist, and in due course of time add immeasurably to the world's wealth and welfare.

As I have said, it is the aim of the physicist to delve deep into the nature of things, and in doing so he has to concern himself with matters which to the uninitiated might seem very remote indeed from the affairs of the workaday world. As an illustration I shall speak to you this evening on the study of cosmic rays, a subject which today is occupying the attention of many eminent physicists. My listeners may remember that we had recently staying with us at Bangalore Prof. R. A. Millikan who is a leading pioneer in the study of these rays. Prof. Millikan came out to India with his assistants specially to study the cosmic ray effects in our latitudes in the hope of getting some light on the origin of the cosmic radiation. This appears to be very mysterious yet, but the study of the effects produced by cosmic rays has already been most fruitful for physics in many ways. The total energy received by the earth as cosmic radiation is about the same as that which comes to us every night as starlight and may not therefore seem at first sight particularly significant. But actually, it is most significant because of the form which it takes, namely in discrete units expressible in many millions or even billions of electron volts, a quantity which is immensely larger than anything that can be produced in our laboratories even with the most modern equipment. It is this enormous energy of the individual particles or units that invests the study of the cosmic radiations with extreme interest, opening out as it does the possibility of observing phenomena which we could never hope to reproduce in our laboratories.

When the cosmic rays enter our atmosphere or pass through any material obstacle, they produce showers of secondary particles, consisting of pairs of positively and negatively charged electrons. The positively charged electron which is also called the positron was in fact first discovered as the result of cosmic ray studies. Another very remarkable discovery recently made is that of a special particle called variously the heavy electron, the mesotron or the meson, the existence of which has in fact been established by cosmic ray studies. This new particle appears to have the remarkable property of changing over spontaneously to an ordinary electron, and has thus in itself only a very temporary existence. A British physicist has recently succeeded in photographing the track of the heavy electron in a cloud chamber at the very instant at which it was doing this transformation trick and converting itself into an ordinary electron.

The cosmic rays also appear to be able, rather occasionally, to cause the emission from ordinary matter of charged particles which are much heavier than either the ordinary electron or the mesotron. The nature of these heavy particles is not yet fully established, but at least in some cases they appear to be protons, that is to say the positivity charged kernels of hydrogen atoms which presumably have been produced and torn off from the kernels of the atoms of other chemical elements present in the material through which the cosmic rays pass.

Very ingenious methods have been employed for the study of these cosmic rays. One of them, which I have just mentioned, is the cloud chamber. In this apparatus, an enclosed volume of moist air through which the cosmic ray has passed is automatically expanded immediately afterwards. The expansion cools the air, with the result that the moisture condenses precisely on the tracks of the cosmic ray particles. The latter thus become visible and can be photographed under an instantaneous flash of light. In some experiments, the cloud chamber is placed between the poles of a powerful electromagnet. The motion of the charged particles produced by the cosmic rays in the magnetic field causes the particles to curve round. From a careful study of the curvature and density of the tracks as thus photographed, it is possible to infer the nature, electric charge and energy of the particles responsible for producing them. One enterprising American physicist recently took himself up in an aeroplane to a height of 30,000 feet together with a cloud chamber, electromagnet and camera, and succeeded in getting numerous good photographs showing the explosions of atomic kernels by the impact of cosmic rays on them.

Another very ingenious apparatus counts the cosmic ray particles and is called the Geiger counter. It is based on the principle that the passage of the cosmic ray renders the gas or vapour in a tube conducting for an instant, and this conductivity causes an electric current to pass in an auxiliary circuit and work a mechanical counter. By having two or three of these tubes in line, and arranging that they will only work in conjunction simultaneously when a cosmic ray passes through all of them in succession, the apparatus functions in effect as a cosmic ray telescope which indicates the direction from which the rays arrive.

THE NEW PHYSICS

The new knowledge that is reaching us through the study of the cosmic rays is of the profoundest interest to the physicist. That this knowledge will in due course influence the whole scientific outlook of mankind and ultimately contribute to human welfare goes without saying. But the onlookers who do not see most of the game should have patience.

CHAPTER III

SHELLS

GATHERING shells on the seashore would probably be regarded today by many as an amusement fit only for young children. A century ago, however, shell collecting was a very fashionable hobby. Vast sums of money were expended by amateur conchologists who paid high prices for rare and beautiful shells. Many of the collections made during this period have passed by gift to the various national museums where they can now be examined at leisure by students of the subject. I am a collector myself, though not in a large way, and would be happy to be able to infect some of my listeners with the enthusiastic admiration which I feel for nature's handiwork in this field. Some of you may indeed find it worth while to become shell-minded and derive some enjoyment therefrom. Shells may be strange companions, but not so strange or so unpleasant as snakes, which I understand were the topic of an earlier talk in this series.

When you see a dead shell anywhere, please remember that it was once occupied by a living pulsating creature, and was built up, little by little, by this creature around itself as a home and as a mantle of defence in its struggle for existence—a home which grew up with its occupant as the latter increased in size and reached maturity. The study of shells, fascinating in itself, becomes doubly so when we regard it, in its correct perspective, as the study of one of the most ancient forms of life on this planet of ours, a lowly form of life, no doubt, but nevertheless of the deepest significance and interest. The forms, the sizes, the colours, and the architectural characters of shells are manifold in their variety and charm. But the mystery and the interest deepen when we ask ourselves why and how the humble mollusc builds for itself these forms of beauty.

When you become shell-minded, you will soon discover for yourself that the number of varieties of land, fresh-water, and marine molluscs is almost incredibly large. Indeed more than a hundred thousand species are known to science. They range in size from microscopic specimens up to huge clams weighing half a ton and big enough to be used as a bath-tub. The variety of form and colour offered by molluscan shells is unsurpassed by any branch of biological life, so much so that the study of the subject becomes an adventure in itself. The molluscs inhabit not only the vast ocean bed, but also live in lakes, rivers and ponds, where there are thousands of specimens only less interesting than the marine species. There are also air-breathing shells of many kinds which live on the land, in trees and bushes, on the ground in your garden, in short under a wide range of conditions. A brief survey of the varieties found in any locality, whether on the seashore or on land, will open the eyes with wonder at the extent of this form of life. The interested observer, wherever he may dwell, will find in his neighbourhood a sufficient variety of forms of shell life to make their study a source of real enjoyment.

The forms of molluscan life have been grouped by zoologists into five great classes of which two are specially numerous and important, namely the Gastropods and the Lamellibranchs; in the Gastropods the shell consists of a single piece while in the Lamellibranchs the shell is in two pieces which are hinged together. Such common forms of shell as, for instance, the Shank, Turbo, Trochus and Haliotis which are of economic importance belong to the Gastropod class. The so-called pearl-oyster, the clam and the freshwater mussel are Lamellibranchs. There is a third important class which includes such weird forms of life as the octopus, the squid, the cuttlefish and especially the celebrated nautilus with its beautiful shell of mother-of-pearl.

Many of you have no doubt seen sea-shells collected into large heaps and then burnt in order to make lime. This will remind you that the principal material which makes up the substance of a shell is common chalk or calcium carbonate; this when burnt is converted into quicklime or calcium oxide. The chalk which forms the material of the shell is deposited as a secretion by the animal from the edges of its living substance and gradually builds up the substance of the shell. Along with the chalky substance, there is a small quantity of organic matter or horny substance which helps to bind the inorganic material chalk firmly together and give it mechanical strength. The shape of the shell is also in many cases evidently calculated to give the structure special rigidity and capacity to withstand impact without fracture. Apparently, in some cases, even if the shell is accidentally damaged, the animal is capable of repairing the break by depositing fresh material. I have myself seen a nautilus shell which has evidently thus been repaired after damage. I may here mention that the part played by minute forms of molluscan life in collecting the material for building their chalky shells is one of great importance in the economy of nature. Deposits of chalk found in the earth are often composed of minute decomposed shells which have no doubt accumulated under water during the course of ages.

The chalky material of the shell presents a very different appearance in different cases. In the common shank, for example, the substance is hard and white, like porcelain. In some cases, as for instance in the celebrated window-pane oyster, it is colourless and translucent like ground glass. In many cases, again, the thickness of the shell or at least the greater part of it is made up of a beautifully lustrous and iridescent material known as mother-of-pearl, which on account of its beauty and mechanical strength has found extensive use in the arts and has considerable commercial value.

The reason for these remarkable differences in the appearance of a substance which is chemically nearly pure chalk has naturally been the subject of much study. I may say a few words about what is known regarding this matter.

Chalk is, in its natural state, a crystalline substance. You may readily convince yourself of this by looking at a piece of crystalline limestone, which is chemically just chalk. A piece of marble when broken will also have a crystalline appearance at the fractured surface. The natural tendency of chalk to form large crystals is resisted during its deposition on the edge of the shell by the presence of the organic horny matter mixed with it. Nevertheless, it does crystallise, and the larger the size of the crystals, and the more regularly they are laid down, the more nearly transparent the substance of the shell tends to become. This is actually the case with the window-pane oyster, in which the crystals are of considerable size and are laid down with considerable regularity. The substance of this shell is fairly transparent and has actually been used for glazing windows in some countries.

It is also necessary to remark that there are two distinct crystalline forms of chalk known, which are chemically the same but physically different, namely calcite and aragonite. Calcite is by far the more common in nature, and indeed this is also the form in which it appears in the substance of all molluscan shells, except in those parts which exhibit a mother-of-pearl lustre. Mother-of-pearl itself consists of chalk in the rarer form of aragonite, but as exceedingly numerous crystals. These are imbedded in a horny substance forming layers approximately parallel to the surface of the shell. Examination under the microscope shows that there may be twenty thousand or thirty thousand such layers per inch of thickness of the mother-of-pearl. This peculiar structure is the cause of the beautiful lustre of the substance and also of the lively colours which it exhibits. The presence of the horny matter in mother-of-pearl is also responsible for the mechanical strength of the substance and for the ease with which it may be worked on the lathe. It also gives mother-of-pearl considerable chemical resistance. Whereas common chalk will dissolve at once in dilute hydrochloric acid, mother-of-pearl is acted upon by this acid only very slowly. I may mention that real pearls have a structure very similar to that of mother-of-pearl, except that the layers instead of being plane are laid down spherically around a common centre. Pearls are therefore just common chalk with a little horny substance thrown in. But this does not detract from their beauty and value any more than the fact that diamond is just carbon affects the prestige of that gem.

The geometrical forms of shells and the carving of their external surfaces are often exquisitely beautiful. What part these forms play in the life of the animal, or whether this beauty is just part of the exuberance of nature in creating forms of life and endowing them with grace is more than I can venture to say, not being a professional zoologist. Nor can I say anything about the beautiful colourations which the shells often exhibit, not having gone into the subject. There is little doubt, however, that the external form of the shell and the internal architecture of its substance are intimately related to each other. Indeed, an examination of the microscopic structure of the mother-of-pearl derived from the Gastropods and the Lamellibranchs and from the nautilus shows that in each case it is fundamentally different. This appears to be a very significant fact which may point the way to further studies of the shell-substance in relation to the zoological classification of the mollusca.

CHAPTER IV

GEOMETRY IN NATURE

THE CONCEPT of beauty defies abstract analysis. On the purely physical plane, however, we can recognise certain elements of beauty, some of which, such as symmetry and proportion, are geometrical in character. When we survey the forms of living beings, it becomes evident that such geometrical characters form a large part of natural beauty. An essential element of its external aspect, this geometrical character, namely the balancing of right against left, is noticeable in most living forms. In the botanical world, we find other and more highly developed patterns of symmetry which give physical beauty to the foliage and the flowers of plants. Under the microscope, the minuter forms of life, both plant and animal, exhibit an infinite variety of symmetric structures. The study of the humbler types of life, as for instance of the mollusca found in fresh water or on the seashore, reveals to the observer a wonderful wealth of geometrical forms. Nature's artistry, however, does not exhaust itself in producing patterns of symmetry. The beauty of a forest, for example, does not consist merely in the beauty of the foliage and flowers of the trees, however ornamental these may be. The tall straight trunks, the spreading crowns and the interlacing branches of the trees of the forest are other elements of geometrical form which hold and delight the eye of the observer.

In seeking to understand and interpret these creative efforts of nature, we can approach them from two different points of view. In the first place we can consider the biological aspect, which is that of the successful functioning of life. The form and structure of the animal or plant determine its activities, and there can be little doubt that the geometrical characters of the structure serve a biological purpose. The balancing of right and left, for example, is almost universal amongst the living things which move on the earth, sail in the air or swim under water, and we recognise that it serves the purpose of facilitating locomotion. We do not find it, for example, in the mollusca which are content to attach themselves to solid supports, and are indeed provided with a special adhesive mechanism for the purpose. We can safely generalise and say that nearly every detail of geometrical form has some purpose to serve in the functioning of life.

The second point of view is that of the physicist and chemist, and concerns itself with the relation between the geometrical form and the nature of the material of which the structure is built. Life has to some extent a choice of building material, but this is not unrestricted, and much depends on the chosen materials being available. The complicated organic compound which is called protein is the very substance of life, but its sensitivity and destructible character make it an unsuitable material for the building of solid structures, except in certain special cases and to a very limited extent. Inorganic substances, as for instance the carbonates and phosphates of calcium, therefore furnish the basis of the rigid framework round which animal life has to function. The nature and properties of these inorganic substances and the manner in which they are associated with the protein substance is one of the essential factors which has determined the geometrical forms of living animals. The protein substance is however adapted for building certain special types of quickly growing structure, as for instance, the horns and antlers of the ruminants and the hair and the wool of mammals. The beautiful silky hair which is the crowning ornament of a woman's head owes its geometrical character of a long continuous fibre to the structure of a certain type of protein molecule. The glory of human hair thus stands revealed as a special effort in protein chemistry made by nature.

I may take the liberty of mentioning at this stage an illustrative example of the relation between external form and the internal structure of the building material, which came to my notice in some recent investigations on the structure of mother-of-pearl shells. It is known that the mollusca may be divided into several different groups in which the shells are of very different shapes. Optical and X-ray studies of the mother-of-pearl derived from the different groups showed it to be completely different in its internal architecture, particularly as to the manner in which the minute crystals of crystalline chalk or aragonite which form the principal substance in mother-of-pearl are distributed and arranged. Indeed these differences have been found to be so characteristic as to leave little doubt that the building up of the external form of the shell, so different in the various groups, is in some way controlled by the internal structure of the material.

The geometry of plant of life is largely determined by the properties of that wonderful substance which is called cellulose. This material is a compound of carbon, oxygen, and hydrogen akin to sugar in some respects but with very different properties. Whereas sugar is soluble in water, cellulose is not, and its molecules are so built that they readily form groups, or micelles as they are called, which can join together and build elongated fibres. Cellulose fibres, cemented together by an amorphous substance called lignin, form the woody structure of trees and plants. When therefore we admire the tall trunks of the giant trees and the wonderful geometric tracery of the branches and leaves in a forest, it is not inappropriate to remember that this wealth of beauty is made possible by the geometry of the cellulose molecule.

I chose to speak to you first about the geometry of living forms, as undoubtedly we are here on more familiar ground. Inevitably the topic led us to the structure of living matter and the nature of the complicated chemical substances which play a part in life. Actually, however, it must be said that we know rather less about such things than about the geometrical forms of the ultimate particles of matter, namely the atoms and molecules, in spite of the fact that these latter entities are beyond the range of our direct observation. During the past twenty years, there has been a very great advance in theoretical and experimental physics, which has enabled us to obtain a precise knowledge of the structure and geometrical configuration of atoms and of many molecules. Theory and experiment alike indicate that the atoms of matter are built up on a regular geometric plan, of electron groups surrounding a central charged nucleus. The building up of molecules by the joining together of atoms also takes place on definite geometrical principles. We have today available physical methods of study by which the form of a molecule and its symmetry of structure can be precisely ascertained and stated. We can for example demonstrate that the molecule of benzene which is the starting point of many complicated organic preparations is, in form and structure, a perfect hexagon.

I come last to the beautiful and intimate relationships between geometry and nature knowledge found experimentally to exist in the study of the crystalline form of matter. When you visit the geological museum, you will see exhibited beautiful examples of natural crystals, as for instance octahedral crystals of diamond, hexagonal columns of quartz, cubes of rock-salt, rhombohedra of calcspar, dodecahedrons of garnet, and huge prismatic plates of mica, to mention only a few items. Indeed, nearly all solids known to nature or made by man are essentially crystalline in structure, though not always in external form. Modern research has revealed the internal architecture of crystals to be an array in space of atoms or molecules, piled up, row after row, column by column and layer upon layer in perfect order and with equal spacing. Geometrical theory enables us to discuss the possibilities of such regular arrangement of the ultimate particles of matter and to classify crystals according to the types of external or objective symmetry which they exhibit, and also according to the types of internal arrangement or grouping of the particles of matter within them. It is astonishing but very satisfactory that the 32 different crystal classes and the 230 different types of internal grouping of particles indicated to be possible by pure geometrical reasoning are precisely the numbers respectively of crystal classes and of atomic groupings which have been found by experimental study to exist in solids.

Chapter V

LIGHT AND COLOUR IN NATURE

THE FACE OF NATURE as presented to us is infinitely varied, but to those who love her it is ever beautiful and interesting. The blue of the sky, the glories of sunrise and sunset, the ever-shifting panorama of the clouds, the varied colours of forest and field, and the star-sprinkled sky at night—these and many other scenes pass before our eyes on the never-ending drama of light and colour which Nature presents for our benefit. The man of science observes Nature with the eye of understanding, but her beauties are not lost on him for that reason. More truly it can be said that understanding refines our vision and heightens our appreciation of what is striking or beautiful. Many a time also has it been the case that the study of natural phenomena has pointed the way to a far-reaching advance in the knowledge. Nature, for instance, provides us, during thunderstorms, with a most striking demonstration of the power of electricity to generate light in its passage through matter. It may be recalled that it is the same power which is harnessed today in a dozen different ways for the service of mankind by our electrical industries.

Another illustration may be given. Looking at the

sky on any dark night, we see a great number of bright points of light of varied brightness and colour which we designate the stars. It is the examination through the spectroscope of the light received from the stars, the general similarity of their spectra to that of sunlight, and the variation in detail of the spectral characters with their colour and absolute brightness, that has been the principal means of revealing to us the stellar nature of our Sun, or if we prefer to so put it, the solar nature of the distant stars, and thereby of establishing the essential similarity of the different parts of the Universe, and tracing the process of stellar evolution.

An interesting field of inquiry which suggests itself to the scientific investigator is the question of the origin of the colour of various objects in nature with which we are familiar. We shall now consider some typical problems of this kind.

It is necessary for us to be clear on one point. What is meant by the colour of an object? Is it the colour of the light reflected by the surface of the object, or is it the colour of the light which has passed through it, or the colour of the light diffused within its interior, and thence emerging? It may seem surprising to raise so many questions about what appears at first sight to be a simple matter. Actually, however, the colour of a substance as defined in these three ways may be entirely different. A typical example is the colour of water. The light reflected by the surface of water is evidently of the same colour as the light falling on it. If, for instance, sunlight falls on the surface of water, the reflected light will be of the same colour as sunlight. The colour of a beam of white light which has passed through a column of water will on the other hand be influenced by any specific absorption which water may possess for the different parts of the solar spectrum. Actually, even the purest water exercises a sensible absorption for the red and yellow rays of the spectrum. Hence, sunlight which has passed through a long column of water exhibits a distinct greenish tinge. Then again, the passage of light through water is attended by a diffusion of the light, firstly by any suspended particles and secondly by the molecules of the water themselves. If the suspended particles are sufficiently small in number and therefore of negligible importance, the diffusion of light within the water will be due principally to the molecules of the water, and the colour of the diffused light will be a sky-blue colour.

It thus becomes evident that the colour of water as seen in any particular circumstances depends on the extent to which the reflection of light at its surface, the specific absorption of the red and yellow rays of the spectrum in the passage of the light through the water, and finally, the diffusion of light within the interior of the liquid, determine the observed effects. It is not surprising therefore that the apparent colour of even the clearest water varies with the circumstances of observation. If the surface reflection is eliminated, as for instance, by looking vertically downwards, and the water is sufficiently clear and sufficiently deep, then the colour is determined by the joint effects of absorption and diffusion by the molecules and is of a dark blue colour, much deeper than the blue of even the clearest sky. If on the other hand, only relatively small depths come into play, as for instance, when the water is churned up and is full of air bubbles or is contained in a relatively shallow basin, the diffusion effect becomes negligible and the water appears green or greenish blue.

This detailed consideration of the colour of water is by way of illustrating the general principles of the subject, and emphasising the fact that an object may exhibit vivid colour and may yet not be coloured at all in the sense of exercising any genuine absorption over any part of the spectrum of the light passing through it. The colour of the blue sky and the gorgeous colours exhibited by the sky and the clouds at sunrise and sunset are typical examples of how the diffusion of light by small particles or by the molecules of matter acting preferentially on the shorter wave-lengths in the solar spectrum give rise to vivid colours. The colour of the diffused light is blue, while the colour of the light which escapes diffusion is determined predominantly by the longer waves in the solar spectrum, and is thus yellow, orange or red, which are the familiar sunset colours.

The diffusion of light in the earth's atmosphere, whether by the molecules of the air or by the particles of dust or watermist suspended in it, plays a large part in determining the general appearance of a landscape and especially of the more distant parts. A surprisingly large part of the illumination which reaches the eye is due not to the distant object towards which the eye is directed, but to the light diffused by the intervening atmosphere. The elimination of this diffuse light should greatly improve the visibility of the distant object. This may be effected by using a nicol or polaroid suitably held in front of the eye. This device quenches a considerable part of the diffuse illumination due to the atmosphere and enables the distant object to be more clearly seen. The same result is even more efficiently achieved by the use of a deep red or so-called infra-red filter placed in front of the eye or of the lens of the photographic camera. The startling increase in clearness of distant landscapes which may be attained in this way is well known.

Broadly analogous to the colour of water is the colour exhibited by the large masses of clear ice found in glaciers and in icebergs. Laboratory experiments show that a beam of sunlight in passage through clear ice undergoes diffusion, the track of the light appearing of a sky-blue colour. The specific absorption of the red and yellow rays of the spectrum characteristic of pure water is also probably shared by ice. The absorption and diffusion effects combine to give the varied colours, ranging from a light green to a dark blue, characteristics of ice of various depths and clearness.

CHAPTER VI

THE SENSATIONS OF LIGHT AND COLOUR

AMONGST the means which Nature has provided for us to enable us to become conscious of our surroundings, the sensations of light and colour occupy a position of supreme importance. The Sun by day and the Stars by night are the power plants from which flow the streams of light which illuminate our surroundings. Not content with these natural sources, man likewise seeks to turn night into day by exercising his ingenuity and providing himself with artificial sources of light of various kinds. The radiations from the sun play a far greater role in our lives than merely enabling us to see our surroundings, but I shall not touch upon that topic now. No wonder, from the earliest times, the tremendous outpouring of energy from the sun has filled mankind with awe and made it the subject of adoration. The source of all that energy has naturally been one of the greatest problems of science.

The first real step towards an understanding of the nature of light is taken when we analyse light by means of a spectroscope. This instrument spreads out the light of the sun into a band of colours traversed by a great number of dark lines. The colours in this band or spectrum, as it is called, varies continuously from one end to the other. The trained eye can easily appreciate fifty or even a hundred distinct tints in traversing the solar spectrum from the extreme violet to the extreme red end.

The spectroscope thus teaches us that the physical entity which we perceive as white light is essentially composite in its nature. To enable the characters of light to be defined in a precise way, we must consider the narrowest possible strip of the spectrum, which we may call monochromatic light. This is conveniently provided for us in the emission from certain gases and metallic vapours when excited by an electric discharge. The sodium vapour and the mercury vapour lamps which are now a feature of the street lighting in our great cities are seen on examination through a spectroscope to emit a small number of distinct monochromatic rays or sharp bright lines in the spectrum.

Various physical experiments, some of which are very simple, show that monochromatic light in its travel through space can be pictured as wave motion with a definite wavelength and frequency. The velocity of light in free space is the same as that of the electromagnetic waves sent out by radio stations. This by itself is sufficient proof that what we call light is essentially electromagnetic radiation, its wavelength being different from point to point in the visible spectrum, but everywhere only a minute fraction of the wave-

length of even the shortest waves used in radio trans-
mission. The physical basis of colour is thus the difference in wavelength and frequency of the electromagnetic waves corresponding to the different monochromatic rays in the spectrum. The wavelength of visible
light diminishes from about 7,000 to about 4,000
Angstrom units as we pass from the red to the violet
end of the spectrum. An Angstrom unit is a hundred-
millionth part of a centimetre.

Light is thus revealed to us as a minute strip in the
whole tremendous possible range of wavelengths of
electromagnetic radiation. It is natural to ask, "Why
is it that we are able to perceive only this highly restricted part of the electromagnetic spectrum as light?"
The answer to this question is, I think, to be found in
a study of the radiations of the sun which is our principal luminary. An examination of the nature of solar
radiation shows that its spectrum extends well beyond
the visible region both towards the longer and shorter
wavelengths; such extension, however, is restricted on
either side by absorption in the earth's atmosphere.
The distribution of the solar energy within the spectrum is determined by what is called the effective temperature of the surface of the sun which is about
5,500°C. If one draws the energy curve of the heat
radiations from a body at that temperature, one finds
that it rises fairly rapidly with decreasing wavelengths
and reaches a peak at a wavelength of about 5,500
Angstrom units and then drops very steeply for shorter

wavelengths. If one were to draw a curve of the sensitivity of the human eye as dependent on the wavelength of the incident radiation for equal energies, one would find that the maximum sensitivity falls approximately at a wavelength of 5,500 Angstrom units. This coincidence between the wavelengths of maximum sensitiveness of the human eye and of maximum energy in the solar spectrum can hardly be considered accidental. If it is an accident, it certainly is a most remarkable coincidence. Indeed, it seems much more reasonable to suppose that the development of our visual sense during the long course of biological evolution has been such as to make the fullest possible use of the actual optical environment provided by the radiations of our sun.

Not merely are we conscious of light, but we also find ourselves in a position to obtain a reasonably accurate idea of our surroundings by means of our vision. Particularly remarkable is the fact that we get a three-dimensional picture of our surroundings and that we can at will fix our attention on any desired object either far or near. These powers rest on the constitution of the human eye as an optical instrument capable of forming a focussed image on the sensitive screen at its back known as the retina. Our stereoscopic sense of three-dimensional vision is possible because we possess two eyes and the retinal images formed by them are slightly different. It is really wonderful, when we come to think of it, that though two distinct pictures of the external world are formed on the retinae of our two eyes, we do not see double and are conscious only of a single external world. The perfect way in which we are able to direct our vision on any object either far or near and thereby scrutinise it in all its detail is also a remarkable example of how the structure of the organs of vision adapts itself to the demands made upon it.

One of the most remarkable features of our power of vision is its ability to adapt itself to the wide range of brightness in our surroundings. When we pass from the bright glare of sunshine in the open air to the dimly lit interior of a building, the intensity of illumination may fall by a factor of a million to one. If the eye is embarrassed by such a sudden drop in the intensity, it is only for a little while. Soon it adapts itself to the feeble illumination. After a long enough rest in the dark, objects that were invisible at first may appear insupportably bright. Under favourable conditions the sensitivity of the human eye is indeed amazing.

If the world we live in were just made up of whites and greys and blacks, it would indeed be a very dull world. Our capacity to appreciate differences in colour adds enormously to the pleasure with which we are conscious of our surroundings. As mentioned earlier, the physical basis of colour is the difference in wavelength and frequency corresponding to the different parts of the solar spectrum. But this statement covers but a very small part of our experience in regard to the actual sensations of colour. It is a question of great interest why a comparatively small change of wavelength or frequency should produce such profoundly different sensations in the human eye. We may also wonder that the physiological mechanism is which enables the eye to be conscious of such differences. In this connection it is very noteworthy that in actual practice we are but rarely concerned with the monochromatic tints of the spectrum. An object may appear vividly coloured, but on examination by a spectroscope may show all the colours of the spectrum. The blue colour of the sky is a typical illustration. Colour regarded as a sensation is generally the result of a distribution of intensity in the spectrum different from that found in standard white light.

The study of colour regarded as a physiological sensation is a subject of great interest. It is also of much practical importance. As typical examples of the striking facts met with in the study of colour, we may mention the following: The colour of yellow light may be counterfeited by mixing spectral red and spectral green. White light may be counterfeited by mixing spectral yellow and spectral violet in a hundred to one ratio. Every known hue can be counterfeited by the appropriate mixture of three primary or spectral colours, one red, one green and one blue or violet. The wavelengths of the colours chosen as primary can be varied to a considerable extent and they may also be broad spectral bands instead of monochromatic rays.

No account of light and colour is complete which does not consider the visual phenomena coming under the general descriptions of illusion and visual fatigue. These play a great part in the sensations experienced by us when we view variously illuminated or coloured objects. They also play an important part in determining the effects known as contrast, visual harmony and clash which arise when different colours are placed adjacent to each other and play a vital part in visual aesthetics.

Some mention must also be made of the interesting condition known as colour blindness which afflicts some unfortunate individuals and prevents them from recognising differences of colour which are patent to normal sighted persons. To be colour-blind may be dangerous in certain types of employment. That is one of the reasons why its study has received much attention. It is also of interest as it throws some light on the phenomena of normal colour vision.

Of recent years, many exact studies have been made of the reactions of the eye to light. Attempts have also been made to translate the actual facts of vision into a theory of visual processes and sensations. Such theories largely rest on the known structure of the retina and the presence in it of certain hypothetical coloured materials which absorb the light falling on them and undergo certain temporary chemical changes. It is a fact that a coloured substance called visual purple can be extracted from the rods of the retina of the higher animals and that a solution of visual purple is bleached by strong light. It is this fact which forms the starting point of some of the newer theories of physiological optics.

CHAPTER VII

LIGHT AND COLOUR IN SCIENCE
AND INDUSTRY

To RISE from bed at dawn, work the livelong day, and go home to roost like the birds at sunset may be a splendid way of ordering human affairs. But I doubt if even the stoutest-hearted dictator would venture to enforce this as a rule of life. It might conceivably serve for those who live in the tropics with twelve clear hours of daylight, but would be utterly impracticable in northern latitudes, to say nothing of the Arctic Zone where the sun is not seen for six whole months and only the auroral lights save the world from perpetual darkness. For good or for evil, man provides himself with sources of illumination of his own fashioning with which to extend his hours of activity. The most primitive of these methods is a fire or a blazing torch. In colder climates, the heat which accompanies the light is naturally very welcome. Indeed, it has been suggested that the worship of fire which is a feature of the Aryan religions dates from the time when the parent race lived in the snow-clad wastes of the north.

A good deal could be said about the development in successive eras of man-made sources of light. We in India are familiar with our castor oil lamps picturesquely made in bronze, but now laid out of sight in odd corners of our homes. The old order has passed away and given place to new and varied present-day methods: kerosene oil lamps, gas mantles, carbon filament lamps, metal filament lamps, gas-filled lamps, low-pressure and high-pressure mercury arc lamps, neon lights, sodium lamps, and so on and so forth.

In considering the usefulness of a source of light, there are many points to be noted. Articles of clothing, and it may be said also our complexions, often appear wholly different in artificial light from what they do in daylight. This is not always a disadvantage, as every lady knows and takes note of. From a strictly practical point of view, however, an artificial source of light is best if it reproduces the colour of daylight. Then again, it is vital from the standpoint of comfort that artificial illumination, like daylight, should be as diffuse as possible. Nothing could be more unpleasant than to enter a room and find your eyes dazzled by an intense and highly concentrated source of light. The provision of dome shades and of various other methods of diffusing light is intended to avoid such unpleasantness and make artificial light at least as pleasing as daylight. Colour, if used with restraint and judgment, is also permissible in artificial lighting as beautiful effects are possible with its aid.

As mentioned earlier, the primitive methods of illumination combine the production of heat and light. This, however, is wasteful. We may cause a body to emit light by raising it to a high temperature. The higher the temperature the more light it emits and also the more heat, though the proportion of light to heat increases with rising temperature. The ideal light is one in which the whole of the energy sent out by the source is concentrated within the rays of the visible spectrum. There would then be no waste of energy as unwanted heat. It has often been suggested that the ideal lamp would be something like the glow-worm or the fire-fly which it is claimed emits light without heat. There are many other living creatures provided by nature with their own lamps to light themselves and their surroundings. In the waters of our seas and oceans live many denizens of the deep endowed with what has been happily termed living light. The processes that result in the emission of light by such creatures have been intensively studied of recent years. Perhaps some day our scientists may successfully emulate the luminous fish living in the depths of the ocean and provide us with chemically manufactured light. Indeed, even at present reactions are not unknown which result in the production of light without heat.

The nearest practical approach to the ideal source of light that we know is provided by the phenomenon known as luminescence. A cobbler of Bologna discovered that gypsum could be converted by calcination into a substance that had the strange property of emitting light in the dark. This phenomenon was long regarded as a scientific curiosity and excited intense interest, with the result that it was extensively studied. These studies have taught us a great deal about the phenomenon of luminescence and the methods of creating it. A body is said to be luminescent when it gives more light in a given range of the spectrum than can be obtained by merely heating it up. Luminescence may arise in various ways, the most familiar being the emission of light under ultra-violet illumination. A striking example of such emission is the behaviour of the so-called blue diamonds which when placed in invisible ultra-violet light shine visibly. I have in my possession a diamond of this kind which emits enough light in a dark room under ultra-violet irradiation to enable a newspaper held close to it to be read.

There are also other ways of exciting luminescence in suitably chosen substances. One of them is to bombard the sound by a stream of electrons or cathode rays. The impact of X-rays has a similar effect in many cases. Luminescence is also excited in certain solids by bombarding them with the rays from radioactive substances. Zinc sulphide is a familiar example of this kind.

Luminescence again is broadly of two kinds. The first is the light emission observed during the excitation. This is called fluorescence. The other kind is phosphorescence, or the emission which continues when the excitation is removed. The latter property enables the body to continue shining in the dark, slowly giving up the energy which it has stored up during excitation. Given enough time, every phosphorescent body must necessarily cease to shine unless re-excited.

During the last decade or two, the subject of luminescence has risen to great practical importance in various directions and especially through the development of what are known as fluorescent lamps. Such lamps are essentially electric discharge tubes with a thin transparent coating of a luminescent material on the interior of the glass walls. The invisible ultraviolet radiation generated by the electric discharge is converted by the coating into visible light. Lamps of this kind are already in use at the present time. Though they suffer from certain disadvantages their high efficiency will undoubtedly lead to their more extensive use in the illumination engineering of the future.

Luminescence excited by cathode ray or electron bombardment has numerous important practical applications, as for instance in cathode ray oscillographs, in television receivers and in electron microscopes. The fluorescent screens used in all these instruments have been progressively developed to a high degree of efficiency. With the development of television, further improvements may naturally be expected.

The so-called luminescent paints which have found many applications of an important character are of two kinds, namely, fluorescent and phosphorescent paints. By painting over important points such as doors, steps and dangerous corners with phosphorescent paints, they can be made visible in the dark without at the same time unduly lighting up their surroundings.

While there are undoubtedly some pure chemical substances which can be excited to luminescence, more numerous are the examples of solids whose power of luminescence is dependent on the presence in them of impurities, indeed sometimes of almost incredibly small traces of impurities. A beautiful example is the intense red luminescence of ruby which is due to the presence of chromic oxide as an impurity in the crystalline alumina which is the main constituent of ruby. By varying the nature and the extent of the impurity or impurities present, as well as by suitable physical treatment of the basic material, the colour and the intensity of its luminescence as also its duration after the removal of excitation can be controlled in a very striking way. Particularly remarkable is the discovery that minute traces of nickel present as an impurity have a destructive effect on phosphorescence without materially affecting fluorescence. This is a fact of real practical importance, since in many cases, as for instance in television receivers, an intense fluorescence under cathode ray bombardment is desired unaccompanied by phosphorescence. The phenomenon of luminescence furnishes many fine examples of how investigations undertaken solely in view of their scientific importance have led to important practical developments.

Light, like all other amenities, costs money to provide, and it is obviously of importance that it is provided in the right measure and in the right places. For this reason quantitative measurement is a subject of real practical importance, in which both physical and physiological considerations enter. Rapid methods of measuring light intensity and instruments for doing this work which can be carried about without danger of damage have been developed. One of the most remarkable and useful types of photometer is an electrical one which depends on the power of light when it falls upon semi-conductors such as selenium and cuprous oxides to cause a flow of current through a closed circuit without the use of any electric batteries. All that is needed is the photo cell which works on this principle and a sensitive electric current meter. The two can be very readily combined into a single handy instrument.

The quantitative measurement and specification of colour is of scarcely less practical importance than simple photo-metry. The skill and judgment with which a trained specialist discriminates between different shades and depths of colour is nearly as marvellous as the precision with which a trained musician can distinguish the finest differences in the quality or pitch of musical notes. As in the case of music, so also in the case of colour, our sensations may be analysed into their constituent elements. Beautiful optical instruments have been constructed which enable this to be done and which rival in their sensitivity even the trained judgment of the colour expert working with his unaided vision.

CHAPTER VIII

PHYSICS OF THE COUNTRYSIDE: THE SOIL

THE BASIS of all agriculture and therefore also of human civilization is the soil of our earth. The scientific study of the nature and properties of soil and of the methods employed in its cultivation is therefore a subject of great interest.

Soil is both physically and chemically of complex and variable nature. This is not surprising when we consider its origin and the vicissitudes which it has undergone both naturally and by human agency. The bulk of an ordinary arable soil consists of a heterogeneous collection of mineral particles of all shades and sizes, ranging from large stones to dimensions below the limit of visibility even in a powerful microscope. In general, the number of these particles in a given volume of soil is very great in proportion to its weight. The character of a soil depends largely on the size of the particles of which it is composed. Hence, in the scientific study of soil, a great deal of attention is devoted to what is known as mechanical analysis. This consists in separating the soil into groups of particles lying in widely different ranges of size and estimating their proportions by weight and the numbers in each group. The methods devised for the purpose mostly depend on the rapidity with which particles of different size settle down when the soil is stirred up with a large quantity of water and allowed to stand in a columnar vessel. Descriptive terms such as fine gravel, coarse sand, fine sand, silt, and clay have been used to indicate the different grades of particles in order of diminishing size. The differences in size of these grades are enormous and are most conveniently represented in a diagram on a logarithmic scale.

A soil which can hold no moisture is obviously of no use. Hence, the study of the moisture content of a soil, and of the distribution and movements of the fluid within its volume, is of prime importance. It was formerly thought that the behaviour of water in a soil was closely analogous to the familiar rise of water in a capillary tube, which is the greater the narrower the tube. It was believed that this simple physical principle afforded an easy explanation of the well-known observed difference between drought-prone, coarse-gravel or sandy soil, and drought-resisting, fine gravel or clayey ones. Careful quantitative studies, however, have shown that the capillary theory in its simple form is incapable of explaining the observed behaviour of soil. In reality, the pore space in soil is of a cellular nature, consisting of relatively large empty spaces communicating with each other through relatively narrow necks. The water distributes itself within these cells and necks in such manner as to reduce its free surface to a minimum. The wide variation in the cross-section of the gaps between adjacent soil particles has most important consequences for the flow of water through the soil. It is clear that a very small difference in hydrostatic pressure will readily drive the fluid through the wider gaps, but much larger pressures will be needed to force it through the bottlenecks. Further, for the same reasons, flow from a narrow to a wide section takes place very rapidly, while a flow in the opposite direction is resisted, and indeed ordinarily does not occur, the liquid opposing the motion by a simple adjustment of the curvature of its free surface.

In these circumstances, the filling and emptying of the pores in soil by water exhibits some remarkable features. It occurs in fact, not in a continuous way, but in jerks or jumps, and the behaviour of the soil differs according as its moisture content is increasing or decreasing. This lag, or hysteresis as it is called, is readily demonstrated by laboratory experiments with a collection of minute glass spheres or with sand. An important practical consequence of it is that the water in soil tends to resist changes, whether these are in the direction of increasing or decreasing moisture content. Instead of moving through the pores from the regions of high moisture content to low, it will adapt itself to the suction gradient by an alteration of the internal distribution of the water inside the cavities.

The bearing of this situation on the question of water supply to plant roots is obvious. The capillary the-

ory taught that the drying due to water imbibition by
the roots was met by the movements of water from
the moister regions, in other words that the water was
brought to the plant roots. The correct view is however, just the opposite; the plant roots have to ramify
extensively through the soil in search of moisture. This,
of course, we know to be actually the case, and the
tremendous range of root development of a vigorously
growing plant must be seen to be believed.

The correct idea of soil moisture relationships enables us to form a picture of what happens to rain
when it falls upon soil in reasonably good tilth. The
soil is, normally, in the condition known as crumbs or
compound particles. The crumb is an aggregate of soil
particles, especially of the finest ones—the so-called
clay fraction—which display this property of aggrega-
tion to a marked degree. The crumb itself is pene-
trated by minute pores, much smaller than the pore
spaces between the crumbs. If the soil is fairly dry and
rain then falls, it enters the pores of the minute crumbs
in the top layer. The excess rain passes downwards
through the larger and cell-like pores between the
crumbs and, in turn, each layer of crumbs levies toll
on it. Depending on its amount and on the initial
moisture content of the soil, the fate of the rain may
fall between two extremes. It may be held wholly in
the upper layers of the soil, or it may displace water
already in the soil, which percolates downwards until
it reaches the water-table. Each soil crumb can be re-

garded as a minute water reservoir which is actively sought out by the exploratory hairs on the plant's root system.

The plough is symbolical of all agriculture. For an essential part of agriculture is the mechanical breaking of the soil and its preparation by the use of a variety of tools and implements. The mechanical properties of the soil determine the labour involved in cultivation, as also the nature and extent of the operations necessary. These have, at different stages, very varied purposes, and take correspondingly different forms, viz. the initial breaking up of the soil, and the removal of the weeds which have grown up upon it, the levelling up of the soil to prepare it for the sowing or planting of the seeds, the subsequent inter-cultivation and removal of the weeds which would compete with the growing plant for nourishment. The preparation of the soil and the removal of weeds represent a very large proportion of the cost of cultivation. Hence, a study of the methods employed for these purposes is of prime importance in soil science.

The impedance which the soil offers to the movement of a plough varies very greatly with the circumstances. It depends, of course, on the nature of the soil, and particularly also on its condition at the time. A soil which has hardened under the influence of a long drought is difficult to plough, and hence agricultural operations must wait till the first rains have fallen. The depth of penetration of the ploughshare into the soil has also a great influence on the work necessary effectively to plough up a given area of land. Much time and ingenuity have been devoted to the development of improved forms of plough suited to soils of varying nature for different depths and adjusted to the power of draught available. The latter is practically unlimited in mechanised agriculture, but the position is altogether different when the plough has to be drawn by animals. Their physical strength and the number available are then determining factors. Apart from the ploughshare which cuts into the soil, what is known as the mouldboard is an important feature in every plough. Its object is to take up the earth and shear it aside, leaving behind a clean furrow of turned-up soil along its path. The theoretical shape of the mouldboard required to do this in the most effective way has been the subject of much discussion and experiment.

It is obvious that the soil being a porous material will contain gas in its interstices. The composition of the enclosed air will be influenced by various factors, including especially the absorption of oxygen by plant roots and micro-organisms and the evolution of carbon dioxide. Hence, it depends upon the rapidity with which carbon dioxide can escape to the atmosphere and be replaced by oxygen. The expansion and contraction of air owing to temperature changes of the soil, the changes of the pore space in the soil owing to rain, irrigation and evaporation of soil moisture, the action of wind and of barometric changes in the external air have all to be considered in this connection. The aeration of the soil is a factor of great importance for the proper growth of plants.

The varying temperature of the soil is another aspect of soil physics which is of practical importance, since its influence on plant growth must be considerable. This temperature would be determined by the balance between the gain and loss of heat by the soil from various sources as well as by the rate of heat-flow through its substance. I shall have to refrain from discussing this topic here in further detail.

CHAPTER IX

PHYSICS OF THE COUNTRYSIDE: WATER

MAN has through the ages sought in vain for an imaginary elixir of life, the divine Amrita, a draught of which was thought to confer immortality. But the true elixir of life lies near to our hands. For it is the commonest of all liquids, plain water! I remember one day standing on the line which separates the Libyan Desert from the Valley of the Nile in Egypt. On one side was visible a sea of billowing sand without a speck of green or a single living thing anywhere visible on it. On the other side lay one of the greenest, most fertile and densely populated areas to be found anywhere on the earth, teeming with life and vegetation. What made this wonderful difference? Why, it is the water of the River Nile, flowing down to the Mediterranean from its sources a couple of thousands of miles away. Geologists tell us that the entire soil of the Nile valley is the creation of the river itself, brought down as the finest silt in its flood waters, from the highlands of Abyssinia and from remote Central Africa and laid down through the ages in the trough through which the Nile flows into the sea. Egypt, in fact, was made by its river. Its ancient civilisation was created and is sustained by the life-giving waters which come down year after year with unfailing regularity.

I give this example and could give many others to emphasise that this common substance which we take for granted in our everyday life is the most potent and the most wonderful thing on the face of our earth. It has played a role of vast significance in shaping the course of the earth's history and continues to play the leading role in the drama of life on the surface of our planet.

There is nothing which adds so much to the beauty of the countryside as water, be it just a little stream trickling over the rocks, or a little pond by the wayside where the cattle quench their thirst of an evening. The rainfed tanks that are so common in South India—alas often so sadly neglected in their maintenance—are a cheering sight when they are full. They are, of course, shallow, but this is less evident since the water is silt-laden and throws the light back, and the bottom does not therefore show up. These tanks play a vital role in South Indian agriculture. In Mysore, for example, much of the rice is grown under them. Some of these tanks are surprisingly large and it is a beautiful sight to see the sun rise or set over one of them. Water in a landscape may be compared to the eyes in a human face. It reflects the mood of the hour, being bright and gay when the sun shines, turning to dark and gloomy when the sky is overcast.

One of the most remarkable facts about water is its

power to carry silt or finely divided soil in suspension. This is the origin of the characteristic colour of the water in rainfed tanks. This colour varies with the nature of the earth in the catchment area and is most vivid immediately after a fresh inflow following rain. Swiftly flowing water can carry fairly large and heavy particles. The finest particles, however, remain floating within the liquid in spite of their greater density and are carried to great distances. Such particles are, of course, extremely small, but their number is also great, and incredibly large amounts of solid matter can be transported in this way. When silt-laden water mixes with the salt water of the sea, there is a rapid precipitation of the suspended matter. This can be readily seen when one travels by steamer down a great river to the deep sea. The colour of the water changes successively from the muddy red or brown of silt through varying shades of yellow and green finally to the blue of the deep sea. That great tracts of land have been formed by silt thus deposited is evident on an examination of the soil in alluvial areas. Such land, consisting as it does of finely divided matter, is usually very fertile.

The flow of water has undoubtedly played a great part and a beneficent one in the geological processes by which the soil on the earth's surface has been formed from the rocks of its crust. The same agency however, under appropriate conditions, can also play a destructive part and wash away the soil which is the foundation of all agriculture, and if allowed to proceed unchecked can have the most disastrous effects on the life of the country. The problem of soil erosion is one of serious import in various countries and especially in many parts of India. The conditions under which it occurs and the measures by which it can be checked are deserving of the closest study. Soil erosion occurs in successive steps, the earliest of which may easily pass unnoticed. In the later stages, the cutting up and washing away of the earth is only too painfully apparent in the formation of deep gullies and ravines which make all agriculture impossible. Sudden bursts of excessively heavy rain resulting in a large run-off of surplus water are the principal factor in causing soil erosion. Contributory causes are the slope of the land, removal of the natural protective coat of vegetation, the existence of ruts along which the water can flow with rapidly gathering momentum, and the absence of any checks to such flow. Incredibly large quantities of precious soil can be washed away if such conditions exist, as is unhappily too often the case. The menace which soil erosion presents to the continuance of successful agriculture is an alarming one in many parts of India, calling urgently for attention and preventive action. The terracing of the land, the construction of bunds to check the flow of water, the practice of contour cultivation and the planting of appropriate types of vegetation are amongst the measures that have been suggested. It is obvious that the aim should be to check the flow of water at the earliest possible stage before it has acquired any appreciable momentum and correspondingly large destructive power.

Water is the basis of all life. Every animal and every plant contains a substantial proportion of free or combined water in its body, and no kind of physiological activity is possible in which the fluid does not play an essential part. Water is of course, necessary for animal life, while moisture in the soil is equally imperative for the life and growth of plants and trees, though the quantity necessary varies enormously with the species. The conservation and utilisation of water is thus fundamental for human welfare. Apart from artesian water, the ultimate source in all cases is rain or snowfall. Much of Indian agriculture depends on seasonal rainfall and is therefore very sensitive to any failure or irregularity of the same. The problems of soil erosion and of inadequate or irregular rainfall are closely connected with each other. It is clear that the adoption of techniques preventing soil erosion would also help to conserve and keep the water where it is wanted, in other words on and in the soil, and such techniques therefore serve a double purpose. It is evident however that in a country having only a seasonal rainfall, an immense quantity of rainwater must necessarily run off the ground. The collection and utilisation of this water is therefore of vital importance. Much of it flows down into the streams and rivers and ultimately finds its way to the sea. Incredibly large quantities of the precious fluid are thus lost to the country. The harnessing of our rivers, the waters of which now mostly run to waste, is a great national problem which must be considered and dealt with on national lines. Vast areas of land which at present are mere scrub jungle could be turned into fertile and prosperous country by courageous and well-planned action. Closely connected with the conservation of water supplies is the problem of afforestation. The systematic planting of suitable trees in every possible or even in impossible areas, and the development of what one can call civilised forests, as distinguished from wild and untamed jungle, is one of the most urgent needs of India. Such plantations would directly and indirectly prove a source of untold wealth to the country. They would check soil erosion and conserve the rainfall of the country from flowing away to waste, and would provide the necessary supplies of cheap fuel, and thus render unnecessary the wasteful conversion of farmyard manure into a form of fuel.

The measures necessary to control the movement of water and conserve the supplies of it can also serve subsidiary purposes of value to the life of the countryside. By far the cheapest form of internal transport in a country is by boats and barges through canals and rivers. We hear much about programmes of rail and road construction, but far too little about the development of internal waterways in India. Then again, the harnessing of water supplies usually also makes possible the development of hydro-electric power. The availability of electric power would make a tremendous difference to the life of the countryside and enable rural economy to be improved in various directions. In particular, it would enable underground water to be tapped to a greater extent than at present, and thus help to overcome the difficulties arising from irregularity or inadequacy of other sources of supply.

In one sense, water is the commonest of liquids. In another sense, it is the most uncommon of liquids with amazing properties which are responsible for its unique power of maintaining animal and plant life. The investigation of the nature and properties of water is therefore, of the highest scientific interest and is far from an exhausted field of research.

CHAPTER X

PHYSICS OF THE COUNTRYSIDE: WEATHER

To THE DWELLER in the towns, the weather is nothing more than a minor inconvenience which can be minimised by a little forethought in the matter of taking an umbrella instead of a walking stick when going out of the house. I will go so far as to say that the average city dweller is scarcely conscious of the weather except when he is reminded of it in some particularly unpleasant fashion. The changing panorama of the skies, the most gorgeous sunrises and sunsets, pass mostly unheeded by him, for alas, the only landscapes that stretch before his eyes are long rows of tenement houses, and as for the sky, it is only seen in little patches here and there, not infrequently cut across by great bunches of telephone wires. The only stars that he sees at night are those that shine on the silver screen at the cinema theatre, and as for the sun and the moon he knows they are there but does not feel called upon to take notice of them more than he can help.

The weather, on the other hand, plays a vital part in the life of the countryside. Those who dwell in the wide spaces of the earth for ever watch the skies and grow weather-wise, for their work and prosperity, nay their very lives depend on what the skies may bring forth. The cycle of the seasons so beautifully described in Kalidasa's *Ritusamhara* is also the cycle of the life of the countryside in India. If one overslept like Rip Van Winkle in Washington Irving's story and woke up unconscious of the lapse of time, a glance at the agricultural scene in any familiar area would enable the date to be fixed within a week or two. Vast tracts in our country still depend exclusively on rainfall for the possibility of any kind of agriculture. The opening and shutting of the sluice-gates in the sky are therefore the most important events in the calendar of the man who tills the earth in these areas.

A former Finance Member of the Government of India is reported to have said that the budgets he had to prepare and present every year were a "gamble in rain". This expression puts in a neat and forcible way the existing preponderance of agriculture in the economy of India, and the controlling influence of the weather on the same. This relation between the weather and public finance appears to have been the principal reason for the establishment by Government of a Department of Meteorology during the last century. The provision of information about the weather, and especially about the approach of storms capable of causing damage to coastal shipping and of giving rise to destructive floods, was clearly of public importance. Long-range predictions of the strength and distribution of the rainfall associated with the periodical monsoon would also evidently be of value if they could be successfully made. These objectives provided the chief inspiration for the activities of the department during the earlier period of its existence. The development of civil aviation and the consequent need for exact meteorological information and especially for dependable short-range forecasts of regional weather led to an expansion of the department. It is familiar knowledge that the needs of the war have led to an enormous increase of the personnel of the department and also to the imposition of restrictions on the broadcasting of meteorological information. The establishment of a section of Agricultural Meteorology shows that the department has not been oblivious of its possible or probable usefulness to agriculture and ultimately also perhaps to the humble tiller of the soil who has depended in the past on his own experience and weather-sense for the conduct of his operations.

The enormous importance of meteorology to an agricultural country like India will however bear being repeatedly emphasised. It is remarked that so far no Indian university has thought it worth while to provide for instruction and research in this subject. This perhaps is only one more illustration of the existing lack of co-ordination between India's real needs and her educational activities. The widest possible diffusion of meteorological knowledge, and the promotion of an active interest in study and research in

Indian meteorology are I think of vital importance. I would earnestly plead that something should be done by every Indian university towards this object, even if it be only the humble achievement of creating the post of an assistant lecturer on a hundred rupees a month who would be required to specialise in and teach the subject. I think the impression has prevailed in the past that meteorology is a subject in which nothing need be done or could be done except under official auspices. I think that such an impression is without real justification and that much work of great value could be accomplished by academically-minded scientists working under unofficial or university auspices. I have very little doubt also that such co-operation as may be needed from the official department will be forthcoming if it is asked for.

There is some justification in speaking of Indian Meteorology as if it were a subject by itself. This is the peculiar geographical configuration of the country with the greatest mountain masses of the Himalaya shutting it off from the Tibetan plateau on the north, and with the peninsula of the Deccan enclosed between the waters of the Arabian Sea on one side and of the Bay of Bengal, and rimmed by the Western and Eastern Ghats. These features play as important a part in the meteorology of India as they have played in her past political history, and are responsible for the principal characters of the variations of the weather in India, both local and seasonal. It should not, however, be forgotten that the meteorology of India is in reality only a part of the greater subject of world meteorology and has necessarily to be studied in association with it.

The pressure, temperature and humidity of the earth's atmosphere are the factors which control its behaviour and interest the meteorologist. Any distribution of pressure over the earth's surface which departs from the condition in which equilibrium is possible necessarily gives rise to horizontal movements of the atmosphere or winds as we call them. It is evident that if such winds were to blow continuously from one part of the earth's surface to another, the air would pile up over the latter, leaving the former empty. Since this is not possible, it follows that there must be a reverse movement elsewhere, and the most natural place to look for such a movement is the upper levels of the earth's atmosphere. It is this simple consideration that invests the study of the condition of the upper levels of the earth's atmosphere and the movements which occur in them with very great importance in meteorology. It is necessary, in fact, in order to understand what is happening near the earth's surface, to know what is happening far above it, and to correlate the two sets of facts. It is for this reason that it is now a regular practice in meteorology to investigate the upper air by observation of the movements of free balloons and also by sending up balloons containing instruments which automatically record the condition of the atmosphere at the higher levels or send radio signals to an observer below.

The remarkable meteorological periodicities which we refer to as the south-west and north-east monsoons determine the extent and distribution of the rainfall associated with them and are of vital importance to India's agricultural economy. It is familiar knowledge that the rainfall during the monsoon periods is not continuous but occurs at intervals determined by the appearance of what are known as depressions, which form over the sea and move into the land areas bringing with them the much-needed moisture and rain. The appearance of these depressions at properly spaced intervals and the magnitude of the associated precipitation are of the greatest importance to Indian agriculture. Hence, the origin of these depressions and the nature of their movements is one of the interesting and important problems in Indian meteorology.

It should be emphasised also that there is an enormous diversity in the details of the meteorological picture over the different parts of the country. We have, in fact, almost every kind of meteorological behaviour represented in various parts of India. Considering, for example, rainfall, we have the incredibly large precipitation at Cherrapunji, the heavy rains in Bengal and in the Western ghats, the moderate showers in the south-eastern parts of the peninsula, the scanty rainfall in many of the interior areas and the arid deserts which cover parts of Rajputana. In parts of northern

India, we have frost and even snowfall, while in the south, frost is only experienced rarely at the highest elevations. There can be no greater contrast in climates imagined than the unvarying damp warmth of Travancore throughout the year and the alternation of dry torrid heat in summer with biting cold tempered by bright sunshine in winter which we find in great areas of Northern India. There is, in fact, what we may call a regional meteorology for different parts of India, the study of which in relation to the practical problems of life in those areas is of obvious importance.

In concluding this talk, let me once again stress the very great importance of awakening an interest in the study of meteorology and especially of Indian meteorology in our universities and appeal for increased attention to the subject by teachers and students alike. I feel sure that active study and investigation in the subject will prove fruitful both from a purely scientific point of view and also from the standpoint of the promotion of India's most vitally important industry, namely agriculture.

Chapter XI

THE ROMANCE OF GLASS

THE DEVELOPMENT of industries is a subject attracting much attention in India today. In view of this, I propose in my talk tonight to review a book the contents of which illustrate in a striking manner the inter-relations between science and industry. The title of the book is *The Properties of Glass*, and the author is Mr. G. W. Morey, who is on the staff of the Geophysical Laboratory of the Carnegie Institute at Washington. It is a substantial volume of some 560 pages and is the seventy-seventh of the series of Scientific and Technologic Monographs issued by the American Chemical Society. The book has been published by the Reinhold Publishing Corporation of New York and is priced at 12 dollars 50 cents.

The glass industry, as Mr. Morey tells us in the first chapter of his book, goes right back to the dawn of human civilization. Glass is found in nature in the form of the mineral obsidian, and primitive man learnt by experience that this substance is easily broken into sharp, often elongated, pieces which lend themselves readily to the fashioning of arrow-heads, spear-heads and knives; its use for such purposes by people of Stone-Age culture was widespread. The beginnings of the artificial manufacture of glass also go back to a remote period of human history. It would appear that the early civilizations of China, Mesopotamia and Egypt share the honour of having discovered how to make glass. The manufacture of glass utensils was a well-established industry in the days of the early Roman empire, and glass had indeed then become a common material in household use. During the middle ages, Venice became a great centre of the glass industry and built up a reputation for skilled craftsmanship and beauty of design which has survived to the present day.

Mr. Morey tells us that the progress of glass manufacture during the nineteenth century was to no small extent the result of the importance to science of the particular variety known as optical glass. The actual quantity of glass used in the construction of optical instruments is but a small part of the total glass production. But the requirements as regards quality in this respect are very exacting. Optical glass must be free from unmelted particles, and from air bubbles, and must be completely homogeneous or uniform. It should also be free from colour and have a refractive index and dispersion for light which have been specified in advance. The production of glass meeting these very exacting requirements has contributed enormously to our knowledge of glass technology, and this in its turn has reacted towards the improvement of all types of glass. In this advance the outstanding contribution was that made by the joint efforts of Schott and Abbe at Jena in Germany. As is well known, these two investigators succeeded in developing many new glasses having special optical properties and thereby brought about a revolution in the optical industry. Incidentally, the new knowledge they created benefited the whole glass industry.

When the making of glass was a manual operation requiring much skill and labour, it was natural to regard glass almost as a precious material and to use it chiefly for making jewellery and ornamental objects. These primitive uses of glass have survived to this day, but they are just a few of the vast number of useful applications to which glass is now devoted. The replacement of manual operations by mechanised automatic processes during the present century has played a large part in the expansion of the use of glass. At the present time, bottles, jars, tumblers, chimneys, globes, bulbs and radio-tubes are made by machine on an enormous scale, while heavy ware is made by moulding glass in furnaces with automatic feeding. Even standard laboratory ware is also often made by machine.

The practical utility of glass for a great variety of purposes is evidently the result of the fact that this material possesses several valuable physical properties. Amongst these are the possibility of fashioning glass into any desired shape at a moderately high tempera-

ture and its capacity for retaining the form given to it
on cooling down, its impermeability to gases and
liquids alike, its chemical durability against the action
of wind, water and even of corrosive chemicals, its
elastic and mechanical strength, its capacity to resist
large changes of temperature, its hardness, its transparency to a considerable part of the spectrum, the
wide range of colours which can be given to it, and its
electrical resistivity. Scientific investigation has shown
that every one of these properties is determined by the
chemical composition of the glass and can be controlled and is capable of being varied over a wide
range by adjustment of the chemical composition. Indeed, great improvements have already been effected
in glass by such studies. I might mention in this connection the outstanding work accomplished by the
Corning Glass Company of America, as a result of
which the mechanical strength, thermal endurance
and chemical resistivity of glass have been enhanced
to a most remarkable extent. Every one of you must be
familiar with what is known as pyrex glass, as also with
the great achievement of the Corning Glass Company
in successfully casting and annealing the gigantic two-
hundred inch glass mirror for the telescope of the
Mount Palomar Observatory in California.

Mr. Morey is not only quite familiar with, but also
evidently deeply interested in the manufacturer's point
of view. His book is devoted to a systematic presenta-
tion and discussion of the available data regarding the

properties of glass. Some twenty different physical characters, most of which are of practical importance, are dealt with in as many separate chapters. The data refer not only to well-known commercial types of glass, but also to special experimental glasses of relatively simple composition chosen with a view to elucidate the scientific principles involved. Many of the results set out are those obtained by the author himself and his colleagues in their investigations at the Geophysical Laboratory at Washington. On going through the book, one feels no surprise at the statement in the preface that the task of preparing the monograph took Mr. Morey fourteen years of hard work.

The last chapter, which deals with the constitution of glass, is the most interesting and at the same time one of the shortest in the whole book. This is not surprising because in spite of the intensive research in the last two decades on the fundamental question of the nature of glass, it remains as yet more or less unanswered. The general nature of the problem may be illustrated by comparing the two naturally-occurring substances, obsidian and granite. Chemically, the two substances have nearly the same composition. Nevertheless, they are wholly different in their structure and properties. Granite, as everyone knows, is a coarse crystalline rock in which the constituent particles of quartz, felspar and mica may be readily observed with the naked eye. Obsidian, on the other hand, is a structureless amorphous solid. In crystals such as those constituting felspar, mica or quartz, the ultimate atomic particles are arranged in regular geometrical order, as is beautifully shown by X-ray investigations. On the other hand, in an amorphous solid or glass the atomic particles are distributed in such a way that the X-ray diagram of the substance is essentially similar to that of a liquid. The latest view of the structure of glass is that it consists of a network of silicon atoms joined to each other through oxygen atoms and forming an irregular network somewhat like a badly-made mosquito curtain in three dimensions. The metallic atoms of sodium, calcium, etc. find places for themselves in the various holes in the network. There is no regular repetition in the pattern and hence the structure is non-crystalline. The idea conveyed by this picture, namely that the structure of glass is irregular though on an intelligible plan, indicates that glass need not have a completely defined chemical composition. Indeed, as is well known, the chemical composition of glass can be varied within wide limits. The best glass of all is pure silicon dioxide, that is fused quartz or vitreous silica. Unfortunately this is a very difficult and expensive material and can therefore only be used for very special purposes.

I have said enough to show that Mr. Morey's book is a most scholarly and valuable publication which fully sustains the reputation of the series in which it has been published. It is not an exciting book, and indeed this could scarcely be hoped for in a technical publication of this kind. The lesson which it brings to the reader is that the true path to success in industry is through patient labour guided and sustained by the spirit of scientific research, and not through haphazard and hasty efforts.

CHAPTER XII

ATMOSPHERIC ELECTRICITY

W E READ in the Arabian Nights the story of a fisherman who flung his net and brought forth from the sea a heavy bottle of brass with a stopper of lead and bearing the seal of King Solomon. Curious to know what the bottle contained, the fisherman removed the stopper, and out jumped a gigantic spirit whose head reached the clouds while his feet rested on the ground. The spirit threatened the fisherman with an instant and cruel death, but being persuaded by a trick to get into the bottle, was once again safely sealed up. It had then to obey the fisherman's bidding.

This story of the fisherman and the spirit may be read as a parable telling us how man has learnt to master the forces of nature. Uncontrolled, these forces may be dangerous and destructive, but once mastered they can be bent to man's will and pleasure. Today, for instance, electricity is man's humble servant, performing a thousand tasks with incredible efficiency. This modern miracle, which we take for granted and never even stop to wonder at, has only been made possible by the labour of the scientific pioneers who cast their nets into the sea of the unknown and fished out strange new treasures of knowledge, often at the risk of their lives.

The early history of the science of electricity makes a fascinating story, one of the most interesting chapters in it being the part played by Benjamin Franklin, the celebrated American statesman and philosopher. Franklin first became interested in the science of electricity in the year 1746 when he was forty years old, and made numerous experiments on the subject. The most famous of these was made in the year 1756 when he sent up a kite during a thunderstorm and drew a spark from a key attached to its string. He thus demonstrated the idea put forward earlier by him that the lightning in clouds is an electric discharge of the same general nature as can be obtained on a much smaller scale in the laboratory. Ever since, the study of atmospheric electricity has been continued by generations of physicists with unabated vigour and interest. In spite of the lapse of nearly two centuries, however, it cannot be said that the subject has reached the stage of exhaustion. Indeed, today the nature of the mechanism which produces the tremendous manifestations of electricity witnessed in thunder-clouds is still a subject of discussion and research.

The study of lightning is of great interest both from the purely scientific and from various practical points of view. The destructive effect of lightning is well-known, and one of Benjamin Franklin's best-known contributions to practical science was his suggestion, which was very early adopted in practice, of protecting houses by lightning rods of metal with pointed ends. Lightning also interferes with the smooth working of electrical power-supply lines and with wireless broadcasting. The study of lightning is also of importance in view of its relation to the electrical state of the atmosphere and to meteorology generally.

It is only proper that in comparing lightning with an electrical discharge such as can be obtained in the laboratory, we should remember the tremendous scale of the phenomenon as observed in nature. Electrical machines have been constructed and are actually in use in various physical laboratories at the present time which develop electrical forces of a few million volts and give sparks a few yards long. The scale of the lightning spark exceeds a thousand-fold the longest spark discharge yet produced in the laboratory. We may well wonder how the astonishingly large electrical forces necessary are generated inside the thundercloud.

Observations of the clouds in which lightning discharges occur make it evident that these clouds are involved in a rapid upward movement of the air. Such a movement is characteristic of thunder-clouds and evidently furnishes the mechanical power necessary for a separation of the electricity to occur as between the different parts of the clouds. It is natural to assume that for some reason or other the moving upward current of air carries with it electrical charge of one sign in excess, leaving behind in the part of the cloud below it an excess of the electrical charge of the opposite sign. This separation and transport of electricity from one part of the cloud to the other naturally results in the two parts becoming charged up in opposite ways. The electric tension then increases until the resistance of the air breaks down and the lightning discharge occurs within the cloud.

A clearer idea of the mechanism of transport of electricity within the thunder-cloud is obtained when we remember that large drops of water fall more quickly through air than small drops, and indeed that if a drop of water is sufficiently small it will, instead of falling, be actually carried upwards by the moving current of air. It is obvious, therefore, that if for any reason the larger drops of water tend to acquire an excess of electrical charge of one sign, their movement downwards will involve the transport of electricity of that sign downwards, while similarly if the smaller drops have an excess of electrical charge of the opposite sign, their movement upwards will further assist the electrical separation occurring within the cloud.

Two detailed theories, one due to Sir George Simpson, and the other due to Professor C. T. R. Wilson, have been put forward, both supported by impressive experiments, which seek to show how in the circumstances existing within a thunder-cloud, the moving water drops in the upward current of air tend to acquire electrical charges, the sign of which depends on their size or direction of movement. Into the details of these theories we shall not here enter, as both must to some extent be considered *subjudice*. The presence of two rival theories has naturally stimulated a large amount of experimental work, both in the laboratory and in the field, intended to test the alternative possibilities. Elaborate attempts have been made to measure the actual magnitude of the electrical separation inside a thunder-cloud, and to measure the strength of the electrical fields subsisting within and outside the cloud.

A great deal of most interesting work has been done recently on the nature and duration of the lightning discharge in clouds and the electrical processes occurring within the zone of the discharge. One of the methods used has been to photograph lightning on very swiftly moving photographic films. In this way it is easily possible to separate the distinct discharges which usually follow one another on nearly the same path. Further, if the speed of the film is sufficiently great it is actually possible to trace the development of the individual spark and the sequence in time of its various branchings. These investigations have led to a much clearer view than hitherto of the actual progress of the electrical discharge which constitutes lightning. The use of a cathode ray oscillograph to study the local electric field alongside of the photographic record of the lightning itself has thrown further light on the time sequence of the electrical processes occurring in the discharge.

The subject of thunderstorm electricity takes on an added interest if we accept the view, originally put forward by Professor C. T. R. Wilson, that the electric field which exists in the earth's atmosphere even in fair weather and of which we are normally unconscious, though it is fairly strong, owes its maintenance to the thunderstorms which are constantly occurring at some place or other on the surface of the earth. The electrically conducting upper layers of the atmosphere would also naturally be affected by the state of the atmosphere lower down in which the thunderstorms occur.

The electrical energy dissipated in an average thunderstorm is quite a formidable amount, indeed much larger than that put out by the largest electrical power station on earth. Apart, however, from the fact that thunderstorms cannot be made to order, trying to make practical use of thunderstorm energy is like trying to hitch a tiger to a tonga. I am reminded of the fate of a bright young physicist who investigated the electrical power of thunderstorms in an Alpine valley. The investigation was successful, but the published paper describing its results included an obituary notice of the author, who became a martyr to the cause of science. Numerous attempts have also been made to utilize the electricity of the atmosphere existing in fair weather for practical purposes. But no important success has been attained so far, and the outlook for such practical utilization of atmospheric electricity is not yet very hopeful.

CHAPTER XIII

MODERN PHYSICAL CONCEPTS: STRUCTURE OF THE CRYSTAL

THE ESSENTIAL unity of all the sciences finds a striking illustration in the fact that our knowledge of crystals is derived from the labours of investigators in many different fields of study. In particular, the subject owes much to the explorers and geologists who by discovering natural deposits of various minerals, collecting well-formed crystals and making them available for study have made it possible for others to investigate their properties. The crystallographer has in many cases to rely on their aid for obtaining the forms which form the subject-matter of his inquiries. The furnaces and crucibles of the metallurgist and the crystallising vats of the chemical manufacturer, however, sometimes furnish fine examples of crystallised solids. These resources have to be supplemented by the personal efforts of the investigator when he desires to study substances not otherwise obtainable as crystals. Slow solidification of the molten substance, controlled crystallisation from solution, and suitable heat treatment of polycrystalline materials are amongst the methods which have been developed and used for obtaining single crystals of useful size.

When the crystal has well-developed faces, the measurement of the interfacial angles, supplemented, where necessary, by special tests, enables the crystallographer to discover what is called the class of symmetry to which the crystal belongs. There are 32 such classes theoretically possible, and this agrees with the number actually shown to exist in Nature. These may be regrouped in six or seven systems amongst which the 32 symmetry classes are distributed. In the cubic system for example, there are five different classes differing from each other in the number of kinds of symmetry which they exhibit, which, except for one class, is less than the maximum number possible for a cubic crystal. The symmetry of a crystal is usually made manifest by the number and kind of faces which it exhibits. For instance, in the cubic system the highest symmetry requires that there should be no fewer than 48 faces of any one kind, while only 24 or 12 as the case may be would appear in the classes of lower symmetry. Such large numbers are however, demanded only in respect of faces of the most general kind which are inclined to all the three cubic axes and at different angles.

The assignment of a crystal to its appropriate symmetry class is of importance, as it is an index of the internal structure of the crystal, and is also closely related to its physical properties. The work of the geometric crystallographer is therefore of significance to the chemist and to the physicist alike. It is not to be supposed, however, that the existence of 32 different symmetry classes necessarily involves 32 different kinds of physical behaviour. Actually, for instance, a cubic crystal exhibits thermal expansion and thermal conductivity which are the same in all directions irrespective of the finer details of structure which determine its assignment to one or another of the five possible symmetry classes. The refractive index of a crystal is also the same in all directions for all the five symmetry classes of the cubic system. The 32 symmetry classes may, in fact, be grouped into a small number of categories depending on the nature of the physical property under consideration which are sufficient to describe the behaviour of the crystal. Elastic properties, for example, fall into nine categories, thermal expansion and thermal conductivity into five, and so on.

The 32 symmetry classes include 11 which possess what is known as a centre of symmetry. Of the remaining 21 classes which do not have centres of symmetry, 6 do not exhibit right or left-handedness, while the remaining 15 do. These features in the structure of a crystal have important physical consequences. The meaning of a centre of symmetry is made clear by considering the examples of a tetrahedron and an octahedron. The octahedron has twice the number of faces possessed by the tetrahedron and its figure has a centre of symmetry, while the tetrahedron has not. The meaning of right-handedness or left-handedness is so obvious that it needs no elucidation. In those crystal classes which exhibit this character, we may recognise atomic groupings which remind us of a right-handed or a left-handed screw or a spiral staircase running through the whole structure.

Right or left-handedness in the structure of a crystal usually reveals itself by the property known as optical activity, analogous to the well-known power of a sugar-cane solution to rotate the plane of polarisation of a beam of light passing through it. In crystals not belonging to the cubic system and therefore exhibiting double refraction, the latter phenomenon complicates the optical behaviour. Nevertheless, by the use of a suitably cut plate of the crystal, the phenomenon of rotatory polarisation can be observed readily enough. Quartz is a well-known and familiar example of a crystal showing such optical activity in high degree.

The very interesting and important properties known as piezo-electricity and pyro-electricity when exhibited by a crystal are a clear indication that its structure does not possess a centre of symmetry. What is actually observed with piezo-electric crystals such as quartz or tourmaline, is that when a plate of the crystal is put under mechanical stress an electric charge develops on its surfaces. Vice versa, the electrical charging up of the opposed surfaces of a plate results in mechanical deformation. These effects may be explained on the assumption that the atoms in a crystal are not electrically neutral but carry opposite or negative charges as the case may be; the elastic deformation and resulting atomic displacements produce an uncompensated electric polarisation in the volume of the substance, and hence also a manifestation of an apparent electric charge at its free surfaces. The assumption stated is important, and it should be emphasised that the converse proposition, viz., that every non-centro-symmetric crystal is piezo-electric or pyro-electric is not necessarily true.

A surer test of the absence or presence of centres of symmetry in the structure of a crystal is furnished by its spectroscopic behaviour. It is well known that the vibrations of symmetrical diatomic molecules, as for instance the molecules of oxygen or nitrogen or hydrogen, do not manifest themselves as absorption or emission lines in its infra-red spectrum. On the other hand, these vibrations appear with great intensity in the spectrum of monochromatic light scattered by the substance. These differences are a consequence of the centro-symmetry of the molecule. A precisely similar situation arises with the crystal classes having a centre of symmetry. If a particular vibration of the atomic structure manifests itself in infra-red absorption, it cannot appear in light scattering, and vice versa. In crystals which do not possess a centre of symmetry, on the other hand, the same vibration may appear both in light scattering and in absorption. A complete agreement between the spectrum of a crystal in infra-red absorption and in light scattering is only possible in very special cases.

A beautiful illustration of these principles is furnished by the diamond, which is a cubic crystal. The earlier crystallographers, basing themselves on the fact that specimens having a tetrahedral habit were forthcoming, came to the conclusion that the structure of diamond has only the lower or tetrahedral symmetry and not the full or octahedral symmetry of the cubic system. The fact that diamond does not exhibit piezo-electric or pyro-electric properties later led to the belief that this view was wrong and that the diamond has really the full octahedral symmetry. A comparison of the behaviour of diamond in infra-red absorption and in light scattering however completely vindicates the opinion of the earlier crystallographers. As has been shown in a monograph published recently by the Indian Academy of Sciences, the majority of diamonds have only tetrahedral symmetry, but the interpretation of the positive and negative tetrahedral types which is allowed by the rules of crystallography and which appears to be extremely common results in diamond mimicking the higher or octahedral symmetry. On the other hand, there are undoubtedly some diamonds which are truly octahedral in their structure, as is shown by the absence of infra-red absorption at the characteristic frequency of atomic vibration. The peculiar situation thus arising in respect of the structure of diamond has been found to furnish the clue to understanding a variety of interesting but hitherto obscure phenomena presented by this, the most remarkable of all solids.

CHAPTER XIV

MODERN PHYSICAL CONCEPTS: THE SOLID STATE

IN THE TEMPLE of Karnak near Luxor in Egypt stands a column of granite, a hundred feet high, erected by Queen Hatshepsut to commemorate the reign of her father the Pharoah Thothmes I. It was cut out as a single piece from the quarries at Aswan, transported two hundred miles by river, shaped, dressed and inscribed and finally set up in place. The engineering skill exhibited in handling this enormous piece of stone weighing over three hundred tons, and the exquisite perfection with which it has been worked and polished command our unstinted admiration to-day, three thousand four hundred years after the column was put into place. This remarkable achievement can scarcely have been possible without a thorough practical knowledge of the properties and behaviour of the material acquired by experience. Many of the traditional arts which have come down to us from antiquity in a high state of development are indeed essentially based on such practical knowledge and experience.

The traditional familiarity with the behaviour of solids which we have thus inherited from the past has been vastly added to as a result of modern scientific and industrial developments. Heavy electrical engineering, for example, is based on the discovery that certain metals are excellent conductors of electricity, that certain others have highly desirable magnetic properties, and that still other substances are almost perfect electrical insulators. Structural engineering has to no small extent been advanced by the development of new metallic alloys possessing special mechanical properties. The progress of aviation has to no small extent been aided by the discovery of the light metals such as aluminium and magnesium and their alloys. The optical and photographic industries have made spectacular advances by reason of the successful manufacture of glasses of special composition having the required transparency, refractive index and dispersive powers. The radio industry owes a great debt to the physicist who discovered the recondite property of piezo-electricity possessed by certain crystals, such as quartz and tourmaline. One could go on continuing a recital of such instances to illustrate the intimate relationship between the advance in knowledge of the properties of solids and the developments of applied science.

The essential feature of the solid state which distinguishes it from other forms of matter is the existence in it of permanent groupings in space of the atoms and molecules of which the material is composed. These groupings and their permanence arise from the forces between the contiguous particles being strong enough to resist the disrupting influence of the thermal agitation which exists in all forms of matter. Both the nature of the atomic arrangements and the character and magnitude of the forces which secure their permanence differ enormously in the various kinds of solids. Broadly speaking, we may distinguish two kinds of grouping. Firstly, we have the regular geometric arrangements of the atoms which are characteristic of the internal structure of a crystalline solid. Secondly, we have irregular groupings which are characteristic of a glass or amorphous solid. The distinction here drawn is essentially in respect of the internal structure of the solids; its external form is much less significant. A piece of ice, for example, has usually an irregular external shape. It is nevertheless a crystal or rather, more often, an aggregate of crystals. This becomes apparent when ice is carefully examined in a strong light. The internal boundaries separating the individual crystals can then easily be made out. Better still, we may rub down the lump of ice into a plate of moderate thickness. On placing such a plate between two polaroids and viewing a source of light through it, vivid patterns of colour are seen, making it clear that the ice consists of doubly refracting crystals and is not a singly-refracting glass or amorphous solid.

The great majority of solids we have to deal with in practice are aggregates of crystals. These may be recognised visually in many cases, for example, in a piece of granite or marble. In other cases, however, a microscopic examination may be necessary. Even the microscope may sometimes fail to reveal the crystalline nature of the solid. The use of X-ray methods then becomes necessary. A truly vitreous or amorphous solid is one in which X-ray study does not reveal a geometric grouping of the atoms or molecules even in small elements of volume. In the case of transparent materials, a simpler test is usually sufficient to indicate whether a substance is crystalline or amorphous in its ultimate structure. This is the examination of the material suitably sectioned and mounted under the polarising microscope. If the substance is crystalline or quasi-crystalline in structure, bright areas indicative of birefringence are seen. The vast majority of the rocks in the earth's crust and most of the solid parts in the structure of animals and plants examined in this way reveal a crystalline or quasi-crystalline character. A truly amorphous or vitreous solid, on the other hand, unless it is in a strongly strained condition, appears dark in the polarising microscope.

The nature of the atomic groupings, and especially the character and magnitude of the forces which hold them together, largely determine the physical properties of the solid. Of particular interest are the cases where the entire crystal consists of atoms continuously linked to one another by forces of the same kind as those responsible for the formation of chemical molecules by the union of two or more atoms. As examples of such crystals, one may cite diamonds, carborundum and quartz. In diamond we have carbon atoms joined to each other by what are called valence forces of the same kind as those which play a prominent part in organic chemistry. Each carbon atom is linked to four others tetrahedrally, and so on *ad infinitum* till the boundaries of the crystal are reached. In carborundum, we have atoms of carbon and silicon similarly joined up, each atom of carbon being linked to four atoms of silicon and each atom of silicon to four atoms of carbon, the structure being continued on this plan through the entire crystal. In quartz, each atom of silicon is linked to four atoms of oxygen, and each atom of oxygen to two atoms of silicon. Substances made up on this plan have certain very characteristic properties, one of which is extreme hardness, diamond being the most remarkable in this respect. They have also a very high melting point, and are insoluble in water or other ordinary chemicals. At the other extreme, we have solids made of individual molecules in which the atoms are bound together by valence forces, while the molecules themselves are only held together by the very weak residual forces which they exert on each other. Most organic solids belong to this class. They easily melt or even sublime directly into vapour, and also easily dissolve in appropriate solvents. As examples of such behaviour, we may mention camphor, menthol and naphthalene.

Another class of solids of great interest is that illustrated by the familiar example of rock-salt or sodium chloride. Substances of this class are formed by the chemical union of a strong base with a strong acid, and it is commonly the case that such substances readily dissolve in water and that the resulting solution is a strong conductor of electricity. This behaviour is explained by the hypothesis that the solid is built up of electrically charged atoms or atomic groups, the positively charged basic groups being surrounded by the negatively charged acid groups and *vice versa*, and that the solid is held together by the electrical attractions between these oppositely charged groups. This hypothesis successfully explains many facts and is at least a tolerable approximation to the truth in many cases.

Metals and metallic alloys stand in a class by themselves, and in view of their practical importance have been the subject of an immense amount of scientific research. Special methods have been devised by which it is possible to obtain large pieces of a pure metal consisting of a single crystal or of a very few single crystals. Such a specimen possesses mechanical properties which are very different indeed from the behaviour of the same metal when, as is usual, it is an aggregate made up of an immense number of small crystals. The single crystal is mechanically very weak and is easily deformed by even moderate forces. After every such deformation however, the crystal gains strength, and ultimately becomes as strong as an ordinary sample of the same metal. This property of building up strength

under cold working is one of the most valuable quali-
ties exhibited by metals and is responsible for their
great practical importance. It has been explained as
the result of the breaking up of the original large
crystals present in a well-annealed specimen into a
great number of smaller crystals and their subsequent
locking together into a strong and coherent irregular
structure.

This enumeration of the different types of solid is
by no means an exhaustive one. We have made no
mention of the border-line cases nor have we considered the structure and properties of the so-called
amorphous solids in any detail. One of the most remarkable developments of technology in modern times
is the development of the so-called plastic industry
which deals with the artificial production of substances
which stand half-way between the amorphous and the
crystalline state of matter and possesses very valuable
properties. Chief amongst these is the ease with which
they may be fashioned into various forms and shapes
of practical utility.

CHAPTER XV

MODERN PHYSICAL CONCEPTS: COSMIC RAYS

THE DISCOVERY by Victor Hess, an Austrian physicist, of a radiation from extra-terrestrial sources which far transcends both X-rays and the gamma rays of radium in its penetrating power was made over thirty years ago. The very great importance of that discovery was, however, not at once appreciated. Indeed, it was not until a quarter of a century later that the award of the Nobel Prize was made to Victor Hess for this fundamental work. Meanwhile, the intensive study of cosmic radiation and of its effects on matter had consequences of the highest importance for the progress of physical science. It is not surprising therefore that cosmic ray research is one of the most actively pursued branches of physics at the present time. Indeed, we may confidently expect to look forward to many more discoveries of first-rate importance emerging from work in this field after the war, when the physicists of the world can once again turn their attention to the systematic pursuit of scientific studies.

Whatever may be the real nature of the penetrating radiation, the fact that it enters the atmosphere from outside the earth is a well-established result. This was shown by Victor Hess himself by sending up electrical apparatus in a balloon to record the effect of the radiation to as great a height as possible. Many experiments of this kind have since been made, and it is now clear that what we observe at the surface of the earth is not the thing itself as it is before it enters the earth's atmosphere, but rather the consequences of its passage through the latter. That the effects can be perceived at all after traversing the whole column of the earth's atmosphere, equivalent to a layer of water ten metres thick, is itself an indication of its extraordinary penetrative power. Indeed, its effects can be perceived even after passage through further considerable thickness of matter, as for instance, twenty or thirty metres below the surface of water in a mountain lake.

Some indications of the real nature of the thing before it enters the earth's atmosphere are furnished by comparative studies of the phenomena as observed at various latitudes on the earth's surface. Here again, it has been clearly established that the effect both at the earth's surface and at the highest levels in the earth's atmosphere which can be reached by free balloons depend greatly on the latitude of observation. The existence of the latitude effect receives an explanation if we recall that the earth is a magnet, the field surrounding which extends far out to space, though with steadily diminishing intensity. If, therefore, a stream of moving charged particles travel towards the earth from various directions in space, their paths will be deflected when they traverse this magnetic field. Whether they can penetrate the field and reach the outer levels of the earth's atmosphere will depend on the energy of movement of the particles. It can be shown that the less energetic ones can scarcely hope to reach the equatorial belts of the earth, but will be permitted to arrive in regions nearer its magnetic poles. The differences in the phenomena as actually observed are of the general nature indicated by these considerations, thereby showing clearly that we are dealing with a stream of electrically charged particles and not with electromagnetic radiation, since the latter would be entirely uninfluenced by the earth's magnetic field. There is also distinct evidence that the particles enter the earth's atmosphere in a direction having a bias towards the west of the vertical. Hence, it may be inferred that the particles are positively charged, and are presumably protons, in other words the charged nuclei of hydrogen atoms.

It is well known that when swiftly-moving charged particles traverse a substance such as common air which is ordinarily non-conducting, the latter is ionized, in other words, temporarily becomes an electrical conductor. An analogous effect is also produced by high-frequency radiation, such as X-rays or the gamma rays of radium, the ionisation in this case being a secondary effect due to the charged particles ejected from the atoms of matter by the impact of the radiation. All the various methods of study of cosmic radiation which have been devised and employed so far depend directly or indirectly on this ionising power of swiftly-moving charged particles. The details of the process depend to a very great extent on the energy of the particles or the hardness of the radiation as the case may be. With the hardest gamma rays, for example, we can observe effects of a kind which are not noticeable with X-rays. Then again, the energies of the individual particles met with in the cosmic ray field are so enormously larger than those found with even the hardest gamma rays, that we have to deal with a wide variety of new phenomena which the latter are incapable of producing.

The extremely ingenious kinds of apparatus used in cosmic ray studies may broadly be placed in three divisions: the recording electroscopes which register the ionisation produced; the Geiger counters which actually register the number of individual particles observable under determined conditions; the Wilson chamber which exhibits the actual tracks of the particles in the form of a trail of water droplets condensed on their path, thereby making them visible. The Wilson chamber with the assistance of a powerful magnetic field which curls up the tracks of the moving charged particles also enables their energy of movement and the sign of their electric charge to be evaluated. The Wilson chamber method is by far the most spectacular method of the three, since the tracks of the particles can be seen and photographed. Wonderful pictures showing showers of particles, curving in different ways and in circles of different radii corresponding to different energies, have been obtained and published. It was in this way that Anderson discovered the existence of the positron or positively charged electron, and also that the production of positron-negatron pairs by the impact of hard electromagnetic radiation on matter was demonstrated. It was in this way also that the existence of the so-called meson or heavy electron was first convincingly proved. A different method of recording the tracks of cosmic ray particles and of the products of their collision with matter has also been employed. This is the very simple one of exposing a photographic plate with a specially prepared thick emulsion for a long time under cover. Very striking records have also been obtained in this way.

The Geiger counter is a most ingenious and powerful instrument. It is essentially a cylindrical tube containing a suitable gas or vapour and carrying a fine tungsten wire along its axis. The entry of an ionising particle acts like a trigger and sends an electric flash through the tube. This is followed by an automatic clean-up and the tube is ready again after an incredibly short time for the next particle. By the use of relays and other devices, these flashes can be counted individually or in groups and recorded mechanically. Whole batteries of counters connected in various ways are employed to determine the circumstances of production of the secondary cosmic ray particles, their penetrative power and the direction of their travel. Groups of Geiger counters arranged in rows or in trays have been employed, in fact, like cosmic ray telescopes. When we enter cosmic ray research room, as for instance the one set up at Bangalore by my young friend Mr. Vikram Sarabhai, and hear the counters ticking away, the universal presence of the cosmic radiations is brought home to the observer in the most vivid manner.

In some respects, cosmic ray research stands apart from other types of experimental studies in physics. It is, of course, possible to carry out certain types of work on the subject within the four walls of an ordinary laboratory. But these are rather restricted in character. More often the cosmic ray physicist has to become a traveller, a mountain climber, an aviator or a stratosphere balloonist and carry his apparatus to various places on the earth's surface or high up above it to find out what is happening there. He may have also to transport his apparatus to places or heights which he cannot hope to reach personally, and has then to devise portable outfits which can be so carried and which can automatically record the results or automatically send out signals which can be received and recorded for subsequent leisured study. The sending up of free balloons into the heights of the stratosphere carrying such apparatus is a familiar procedure in cosmic ray research. It has greatly assisted in discovering the nature of the transformations the energy associated with the primary particles undergoes as it penetrates to the lower levels of the earth's atmosphere.

The energy of the individual cosmic ray particle before it enters the earth's atmosphere has been estimated to be of the order of thousands of millions of electronvolts, while the greatest energies which have so far been generated in the laboratory have been about fifty million electronvolts. It is not surprising therefore that the study of cosmic radiation has opened new vistas of knowledge which would have otherwise remained inaccessible. Where the particles with these incredibly large energies come from, when and how they were produced, is still a mystery, and it would be profitless to traverse the various speculations that have been put forward regarding these questions. Suffice it to say that they present us with a problem that challenges the human intellect, the solution of which will undoubtedly carry us nearer an understanding of the nature and origin of the universe we live in.

Chapter XVI

THE STELLAR UNIVERSE

ON ANY clear dark night we see the sky studded with stars, a few very bright ones, many more not so bright, and a much larger number of faint ones. Particularly impressive is the so-called Milky Way which runs as an irregular belt of luminosity across the sky and is specially conspicuous in certain areas as, for instance, in the vicinity of the constellation Sagittarius. A good pair of binoculars reveals much more in the sky than can be seen by the naked eye. Large areas of vague luminosity are seen resolved into great numbers of distinct stars, while objects such as star-clusters and nebulae which can scarcely be glimpsed by the unaided vision become clearly visible. Using more powerful telescopes, our view of the stellar universe is progressively enlarged. The great telescopes employed in the leading observatories of the world and especially the photographs obtained with their aid reveal to us a picture of almost incredible magnificence. The reproductions of photographs of the sky which illustrate modern treatises on astronomy convey some idea of the power of the great instruments with which they have been obtained.

The exploration of the stellar universe and the discovery of its structure, extent, and past history are amongst the major problems of astronomy. To the task of solving these problems the world's leading observatories and the world's great astronomers, both past and present, have devoted their attention. From their work has progressively emerged a body of facts as well as an interpretation of the same, which can scarcely be regarded as final, but which is at least striking and suggestive, and in so far as it is based on unquestionable evidence has claims to acceptance. As in all the sciences, so in astronomy, we have to deal with a vast mass of observational detail and of intricate calculations and discussion. Much of this can only be assessed and understood by the professional workers in the field. The essential ideas underlying the observational work and its theoretical interpretation are, however, not beyond the comprehension of the non-professional student.

An intelligent understanding of stellar astronomy must necessarily be based on a general idea of methods employed in its study. The whole of the science of astronomy, of course, rests on the study of the light of the stars which enables us to perceive them. To the non-professional worker, visual observations and the pleasure which they give are, of course, the very essence of astronomy. I remember myself, very vividly, the two nights I spent at the Mount Wilson Observatory in California twenty years ago. By a piece of extraordinary good luck—as I thought—the condition of the atmosphere was rather poor, and hence the great telescopes in the observatory could not be satisfactorily used for the regular work assigned to them. This made it possible for me to do some sight-seeing. I came away tremendously impressed with the marvellous light-gathering power of the great sixty-inch and hundred-inch reflectors. The great nebula in Orion, for instance, which in ordinary instruments appears as a shapeless area of great luminosity, appeared in the sixty-inch as a luminous patch of variegated colour, determined by the light-emission of the gases of which it is composed.

Visual observation, however, plays but a minor part in the activities of the professional astronomer. Much of his work is done with the aid of the photographic plate on which the star fields are recorded using apertures and exposures suited to the problem under investigation. The apparent daily motion of the stars has, of course, to be eliminated and the stellar images kept fixed on the photographic plate. This is done by making the instrument follow the stars in their apparent daily motion. When we remember the gigantic size of modern telescopes, the mechanical perfection of the driving arrangements necessary to prevent the star images on the plate becoming blurred or drawn out into lines will be appreciated. The great advantage of the photographic plate is that by prolonging the exposures sufficiently, images of objects altogether too faint to be observed visually are recorded on the plate and can be studied at leisure. The effective penetration of the telescope into the depths of space is thus vastly increased.

Stellar photography enables us to locate the relative positions of the stars and also to determine their apparent brightness. Using plates sensitized to different regions of the spectrum, determinations of the star colours can also be made. The nature of the light emitted by a star is however far more effectively studied by recording its spectrum. For this purpose, the spectroscopic apparatus has to be fixed to the telescope or made an integral part of it in some suitable manner. It is found that the spectra of the stars are far from being identical with each other. Indeed, they differ so greatly that stellar spectra have been grouped into ten distinct classes. There is a marked connection between the variations in the spectra and the colour of the stars as seen visually. The study of the spectra, however, teaches us far more about the physical condition of a star than observation of its colour.

Our knowledge derived from observational studies comes under several distinct heads: firstly the position of a star relatively to other stars, secondly its apparent brightness and colour, and thirdly its spectral class. It should not be imagined however that these items in the description of a star remain unchanged for all time. A star may exhibit what is called parallax, which is a small apparent motion in space due to the annual movement of the earth round the sun. This is inversely proportional to the distance of the star from us. The star may also exhibit a proper motion transverse to the line of sight, which results in secular displacements of its position in the field of stars. Farther, a star may also have a movement along the line of sight. This cannot be detected from the photographic starcharts, but is inferred from the Doppler displacements towards the red or towards the violet of well-known standard reference lines in its spectrum. Apart from these apparent or real movements of a star, we often also encounter variations in its apparent brightness. These may be either regular and periodic, or else irregular. The regular variations may be either caused by the components of a multiple star eclipsing each other during their relative periodic movements, or they may be actually due to pulsations in the size of structure of a star. Finally, we may have also variations in the spectrum of a star. These are particularly conspicuous in the spectra of new stars. Less striking changes are also noticed in the spectra or variable stars. The apparent brightness of a star and its real or absolute brightness are quantities connected with each other. They are not, however, identical, since the apparent brightness diminishes with the distance of the star from us. It is clear that from a physical point of view it is the real and not the apparent brightness which is the significant quantity.

A matter of great importance in relation to stars is

the question whether they have any measurable angular diameter. As we see it visually, a bright star appears bigger than a faint one, but this is only a physiological illusion. In the same way, on the photographic plate, bright stars are recorded as having larger disks than faint ones. But this again is only a spurious effect, though a useful one, since it furnishes a convenient and simple way of estimating the position of a star in the scale of apparent brightness. Indeed, the angular dimension of all the stars, except of course our own sun, are far too small to be measured or even detected directly from the size of their telescopic images. It may be mentioned that a special method, making use of an instrument known as the interferometer, was devised by Michelson for measuring the apparent angular diameter of stars.

The method was successfully applied to the giant star Betelgeuse in the constellation Orion. Its angular diameter came out to be the twentieth part of a second of arc. Combining this with the distance of Betelgeuse estimated from its known small parallax, the linear diameter of this star came out as the amazing (though not unexpected) value of 240 million miles.

The determination of the annual parallax of a star is the most direct method of finding its distance from us. Its angular magnitude diminishes with increasing distance of the star, and for very distant stars becomes too small to be observable. The number of stars showing a measurable parallax is negligibly small compared with the immense number of stars whose existence is revealed to us by the giant photographic telescopes. The extreme smallness of the parallax of even the nearest stars, and its negligible size for the more distant ones, emphasize the enormous scale of the stellar universe. Special methods have been devised for the determination of at least the order of magnitude of the distances of the outlying stars and star clusters from us. I shall deal with these methods in a later talk. I shall now content myself with indicating very briefly the general ideas regarding the structure of the stellar universe which are entertained at the present time.

Our sun is, of course, a star, indeed not a very large or a very bright one. Together with its neighbours and several star clusters which are easily resolved as distinct stars in a large telescope, it forms what is known as the local system. This again is only part of the great galaxy of stars which we recognize as the Milky Way. The more obvious features of the Milky Way are interpreted by regarding the galaxy as a kind of spiral nebula composed of stars the central condensation of which we see as the bright patch of light in the constellation Sagittarius. Beyond and outside this galaxy of ours, lie other galaxies in immense numbers and at incredibly great distances. The existence of these is revealed in photographs taken with large telescopes.

The only one of these outer galaxies which is visible to the naked eye is the celebrated nebula in Andromeda. The stellar character of this nebula becomes evident when it is observed through telescopes of the requisite power.

CHAPTER XVII

THE STELLAR UNIVERSE

THE SUN is just a star, but since it is very much closer to the earth than the next nearest star it appears by far much larger and by far much brighter than any of them. When we observe the sun through a telescope, we see a disc that is brightest at the centre and gradually diminishes in brightness towards the edge. This luminous surface is called the photosphere. Its smoothness is frequently marred by the presence of dark spots, whilst at the edges streaks of intense brightness are often observed, which are called "faculae". The behaviour of sun-spots and of faculae has been systematically studied for quite a long time. Their observation enables us amongst other things, to determine the period of rotation of the sun.

If we project the sun's disc on the slit of an ordinary spectroscope, we obtain a continuous bright spectrum cut across by numerous dark lines, known as the Fraunhofer lines. Careful study of the solar spectrum at various points on the sun's disc from its centre up to the edge and even beyond shows remarkable differences. From these, it is inferred that the light of the photosphere has a continuous spectrum and that the Fraunhofer dark lines arise from the absorption of the

[121]

light of the photosphere in its passage through a tenuous layer of vapours, known by reason of this action as the reversing layer. Still higher up, we have what is known as the chromosphere, which emits a bright line spectrum. The best conditions for studying this chromosphere spectrum occur during the precious few minutes when the sun is totally eclipsed by the disc of the moon. Beyond the chromosphere again, we have the solar prominences, and still further out, what is known as the solar corona. The prominences are fairly bright, while the corona is much weaker. They are both visible to the naked eye at the time of total solar eclipses. Methods have been devised using special instruments known as spectroheliographs by which the prominences can readily be photographed even at ordinary times. Quite recently the French astronomer Lyot has developed a technique by which the solar corona or at least the low-lying parts of it can be photographed from high mountain tops at ordinary times.

The systematic study of the sun and the phenomena presented by the atmosphere surrounding it is of very great interest from several points of view. The intensity of solar radiation has naturally an influence on the meteorological conditions on the earth's surface. There is plenty of evidence to show that the well-known eleven-year sunspot cycle induces corresponding changes in the weather on the earth's surface. The solar radiations also influence the conditions at very high levels in the earth's atmosphere which make possible the propagation of wireless waves round the curvature of the earth. Apart from these terrestrial consequences of practical importance to us, solar phenomena are astronomically significant. They enable us in fact to have a closer appreciation of what each of the myriads of stars in the sky really is. The distant stars appear to us just pinpoints of light, and all that we can do with them is to study the total light of the star. On the other hand, in the case of the sun we can investigate the spectrum of the disc from point to point. Such investigations have proved immensely fruitful and have revealed most striking and even startling phenomena. I will only mention one here. That is the discovery made by George E. Hale of the existence of powerful magnetic fields, thousands of times more powerful than the earth's magnetic field, inside sunspots. The existence of these magnetic fields is made evident by spectroscopic observation and can only be explained on the assumption that huge electric currents or the equivalents thereof exist within sunspots.

The temperature of the sun's surface can be estimated from the total radiation which we receive from it, as also by a detailed examination of the energy in the different parts of the spectrum. It comes out as something of the order of 6000°C, rather more than we can reach within the most powerful electric furnaces. High as this temperature may seem, we must not make the mistake of imagining that it is anything

very extraordinary from the point of view of astronomy. As mentioned just now, it is only the superficial
temperature of the sun. There are excellent grounds
for the belief that the temperature must become enormously greater as we proceed inside the sun. It would
take me much too long a time and also far too deep
into recondite theoretical physics to explain how astro-
physicists have sought to calculate the temperature in
the interior of the sun and the stars. It comes out to be
of the order of many millions of degrees centigrade. The
figures are so startling that one might be inclined to
dismiss them as merely speculative. It is of course
quite true that we have no direct means of observing
or determining the temperatures of stellar interiors.
The calculations however are based upon well-under-
stood physical principles and carefully worked out
mathematical investigations. One may therefore feel
confident that they are not very far from representing
reality.

Comparison of the solar spectrum with that of various stars in the sky yields very significant results. Actually, as I remarked in an earlier talk, the spectra of
the stars are far from being all identical. Indeed, they
are so different from each other that at least ten separate spectral classes have to be recognized, which show
enormous differences among themselves. The spectrum
of our sun resembles very closely the spectra of the
yellow coloured stars, exhibiting as it does thousands
of dark Fraunhofer lines. The spectra of the blue stars

are much simpler. The conditions in the atmosphere of the latter are such that the absorption lines of hydrogen and of helium come out clearly, while those of the heavier elements, so conspicuous in the solar spectrum, are scarcely to be observed. The facts on which the classification of stellar spectra are based are exceedingly significant. They compel us in fact to recognize a regular sequence of stars, indicating successive stages in the evolution of these bodies.

We in India do not need to be reminded of the enormous quantities of heat energy poured out by our own sun. The latter is far from being intrinsically either the largest or the most brilliant of the myriads of stars in the universe. We are naturally left wondering where does all this terrific output of energy come from? So far as we can observe, no sensible diminution in the output of the sun's energy has occurred within historic times. It is possible to make a fairly accurate computation of the total output of energy from the sun. When we seek to find an explanation for it in terms of nineteenth-century physics, we are led to contradictions of a most serious kind.

At the present time, it is believed that the source of the energy poured out as radiation from the sun and the stars is to be found in chemical changes of a fundamental character and involving the transmutation of elements occurring in their interior. Theories regarding the exact nature of these transmutations have been developed. They have been apparently successfully linked up with the existence of what I have referred to above as the stellar sequence. Here again, I must refrain from entering into detail, as it would take us too deeply into theoretical complications.

One of the most striking discoveries in astronomy of modern times is the apparent motion away from us and from each other of the distant spiral nebulae. As I mentioned in my previous talk, the great telescopes of the world have revealed the existence of enormous numbers of these spiral nebulae. They are at such great distances that powerful instruments and long exposures are needed to record them on the photographic plate. Still more difficult it is to obtain photographic records of their spectra. This has however been successfully achieved especially with the great 100-inch telescope at Mount Wilson. The distance of any particular nebula can be roughly estimated from the degree of its faintness. Such an estimate would naturally be the more reliable when we consider a great number of such objects. The startling result emerges that the further the object is from us, the more rapidly it is moving away from us. The velocities of recession are indicated by the displacements towards the red of well-marked absorption lines in the spectra. The recession velocities of the nearest ones are of the order of a few hundred kilometres per second. As we go further out, this increases to some thousands of kilometres per second. The faintest and most outlying nebulae show almost incredibly large velocities of the order of 10,000 kilometres per second or more.

There has been a great deal of discussion about the explanation of these amazing facts of observation. Attempts have been made to link them up with ideas basic to the general theory of relativity. Many theorists seem to favour the idea that the velocities of recession indicated by the spectral shifts must be regarded as real. The concept has been seriously put forward that the stellar universe as a whole is rapidly expanding. There are however other theorists who prefer to find some other explanation for the observed red shift of the lines in the nebular spectra. They believe that this shift arises from some hitherto unrecognized property of light, which changes its frequency in its passage through the enormous distances involved. I must refrain from expressing any opinion of my own on these highly debatable questions.

CHAPTER XVIII

THE FUTURE OF PHYSICS

IF SOME eminent physicist who died fifty years ago were brought back to life and invited to attend a lecture or discussion on present-day physics, his first impression would be that nearly everybody was talking the wildest nonsense. He would hear everybody using a lot of words which he had never known before, such as nuclei and isotopes, quanta and photons, protons and neutrons, electrons, positrons and mesons. If he asked a neighbour in the audience what any of these words meant, the reply would be a polite but freezing smile or else a rough remark that he should go back to school. His feelings might be relieved a little to hear an occasional if grudging reference to such old-world notions as the Newtonian mechanics, or the Newtonian law of gravitation. He might even be gratified to discover that Maxwell's electro-magnetic theory of light had not been superseded though it was rarely spoken of or discussed. Most of the time he would find his colleagues talking about the fission of the nucleus, the decay of the meson, cosmicray bursts, heavy particles, the Berkeley cyclotron and radio-active isotopes, and would find it all very, very dreary and very boring, just because he did not understand the language.

If I have been giving you rather a lucid picture of modern physics, it is just to impress on you the tremendous nature of the revolution that has taken place in our science during the last ten years. Vast new vistas of knowledge have opened up, based partly on new experimental discoveries and partly on new theoretical concepts. The physics of the nineteenth century is not dead. But it has disappeared into the background, being overshadowed by the gigantic edifice of the new physics which concerns itself mainly with the ultimate structure of the universe, meaning thereby the infinitesimal entities whose names so puzzled our resurrected physicist. It is the interactions of these entities with each other which constitute all the phenomena of physics and chemistry, not to mention biology. It is the concern of the mathematical physicist today to describe these interactions in the best possible formulae and thereby to predict their behaviour; while it is similarly the business of the experimental physicist to study in the laboratory the reactions of these entities on each other in the most diverse circumstances, to verify the predictions of the mathematician, and if possible to discover new and yet undetermined laws of their behaviour. The progress being made is so rapid that even the most eminent leaders of the science have had scarcely time to comprehend or understand, in its totality, the meaning of all the new knowledge. They can only just glimpse the general trends of progress and hope that they will live long enough to be able to understand it all a little better some day.

In these circumstances, to be invited to put on the mantle of a prophet and predict what is yet to come is rather an embarrassing honour. Indeed it would have been an impossible task, but for the distinguishing feature of physics, namely, that it is not essentially or even principally an empirical science. Physics is primarily a logical system of mathematical thought applied to the elucidation of the phenomena of nature. Essentially, therefore, it is a predictive science capable of discovering phenomena by mathematical reasoning even before they have been actually observed in nature. Indeed, one of the most remarkable features of the new physics is that often the most fundamental discoveries have been anticipated by physico-mathematical reasoning before they have found verification in the laboratory. I may mention as instances the prediction by De Broglie of the wave-like behaviour of electrons, and the meson, which have subsequently found brilliant experimental confirmation. As the latest example of such a prediction may be mentioned that made by Dr. H. J. Bhabha in a theoretical paper recently published by the Indian Academy of Sciences, namely that of the existence of new particles having approximately the same mass as the proton, but having multiple charges. I am fairly convinced myself that this bold prediction will soon find confirmation in experiment.

THE NEW PHYSICS

As already mentioned, the main currents of physical thought at the present time are running in the direction of a deeper understanding of the ultimate structure of matter. Spectacular advances have been made of recent years in the production of new atomic species, that is to say of new chemical elements obtained by bombarding known species of matter with swiftly moving atoms. Probably the most efficient instrument which has been discovered for carrying out such experiments is the well-known cyclotron designed by Prof. E. O. Lawrence of the University of California. The results obtained by Professor Lawrence and his co-workers have been so impressive that cyclotrons have been built in several of the leading laboratories of the world. There is one for instance at the Cavendish Laboratory of Cambridge with which a young Indian Dr. R. S. Krishnan is hard at work, and getting most interesting results. We hear that the Rockefeller Foundation has given Prof. Lawrence a million dollars with which to build a gigantic new cyclotron which will far exceed in power anything so far built. We may anticipate that under the new attack now in progress the mystery of atomic structure will soon cease to be mystery, and that just as the physics of the last two decades has completely analysed the external electrical structure of the atom, so in the next ten years we shall see a complete understanding of the kernel or nucleus of the atom which determines its mass and chemical symbol.

THE NEW PHYSICS

Already the advance of our knowledge of atomic nuclei has brought nearer a fuller understanding of the cosmogony of the universe. The stars which we see dotting the sky in their myriads are in reality gigantic crucibles in which systematic chemical reaction, or I should perhaps say alchemical reactions changing one element to another, are continually taking place. It is already recognised that these reactions are the real sources of stellar energy. There is every hope, therefore, that side by side with the progress of our knowledge of matter, we shall soon attain a fuller comprehension of the past, present and future of our stellar universe.

I think it is also safe to predict that the next ten years will see a vastly increased influence of the methods and ideas of the new physics upon the sciences of chemistry and biology. The physics of the nineteenth century was not deep enough really to explain the phenomena of chemical reaction. The new physics has remedied this deficiency, with the result that chemistry is becoming, slowly but steadily, a branch of mathematical physics, at least in its theoretical aspects. As chemistry is essentially what may be called a bread-and-butter science, its transformation from partial empiricism to the status of an exact science cannot but be of benefit to humanity. The biologist, of course, recognises that physics and chemistry have much to do with his own special field and is indeed constantly using methods and tools borrowed from these sciences. All the trends of the present time indicate that biology is getting closer and closer to the basic science of matter. If we cannot hope to see in the next ten years the mystery of life completely solved, we may at least expect a fuller understanding of its physical and chemical basis.

CHAPTER XIX

THE SCIENTIFIC OUTLOOK

IT IS CUSTOMARY in all branches of science to associate the names of eminent men with the facts and principles discovered by them which form the foundations of the subjects. This practice is found to be useful since it helps to abbreviate and give precision to the terminology of science. It also serves to commemorate the name and fame of the leaders of science whose labours have helped to create a subject. Indeed, this is how the student of science first gets to know the names of the great leaders in his subject. The touch of human interest which the study of science gains in this way is of no small value, since it emphasises the real nature of science as a living and growing creation of the human spirit.

A study of the history of individual branches of science and of the biographies of the leading contributors to their development is essential for a proper appreciation of the real meaning and spirit of science. They often afford much more stimulating reading than the most learned of formal treatises on science. To the teacher, such histories and biographies are invaluable. Whenever he finds the attention of his listeners flagging a little, he can always enliven his class by telling a little story of how this or that great discovery in his subject was made or by recalling some anecdote about one or another of the famous investigators in the field. In this way, the teacher can convey to the student an understanding of how science is made and of the intellectual outlook which is the essence of it.

What is meant by a scientific discovery? How is it made? These are questions of perennial interest which are often asked and to which the most varied answers have been returned. A discovery may obviously be either of a new fact or of a new idea. It is clear however that an unexplained observation is of no particular significance to science. An idea unsubstantiated by facts is equally devoid of importance. Hence to possess real significance a scientific discovery must have both an experimental and a theoretical basis. Which of these aspects is the more important depends on the particular circumstances of the case, and a rough distinction thereby becomes possible between experimental and theoretical discoveries. Rontgen's discovery of X-rays, for example, was clearly an experimental one, while Planck's equally important discovery of the quantum of action was clearly in the field of theory. The manner in which a scientific discovery is made and the attitude of the investigator which makes such a discovery possible are obviously very different in the two cases. This distinction between the attitudes of the experimenter and the theorist is most obvious in the mathematical sciences. It is much less obvious in those sciences which rest more exclusively on an empirical foundation and in which observation of facts and thinking about facts are less easily separable processes.·

The word discovery suggests a dramatic and exciting event, like finding a fifty-carat diamond in a ploughed field, for example. The history of science is indeed full of such dramatic discoveries, the drama and the excitement being particularly manifested in the personal behaviour of the scientist immediately following the event. I could tell one or two stories myself of such incidents in the life of a scientist. The classic story is that of Archimedes who rushed into the street straight from his bath with nothing on, crying "Eureka eureka", when his famous principle of hydrostatics flashed into his mind. The point of the story is the intense emotion aroused by a sense of the overwhelming importance of the new idea. The joy and exaltation felt at such a moment are indescribable. Indeed, such dramatic moments come into the life of even the most devoted follower of science but once or twice in his career. They are the greatest reward of a lifetime spent in the pursuit of knowledge for its own sake. Lesser discoveries come oftener and are a source of profound satisfaction and encouragement to the investigator. But they do not make such soul-stirring drama.

It should be mentioned that the reception given at first to even capital discoveries by the outer world is not always one of respectful admiration for the achievement of the discoveries. One of the commonest ways in which the achievement is sought to be minimised by the unthinking or the envious is by attributing it to accident or a stroke of luck akin to the winning of a lottery ticket. Such comments are of course deplorable and indeed quite meaningless. The idea that a scientific discovery can be made by accident is ruled out by the fact that the accident, if it is one, never occurs except to the right man. The happy discoverer in science is invariably a seeker after knowledge and truth working in a chosen field of his own and inspired in his labours by the hope of finding at least a little grain of something new. The commentators who like to consider discoveries as accidents forget that the most important part of a scientific discovery is the recognition of its true nature by the observer, and this is scarcely possible if he does not possess the requisite capacity or knowledge of the subject. Rarely indeed are any scientific discoveries made except as the result of a carefully thought-out programme of work. They come, if they do come, as the reward of months or years of systematic study and research in a particular branch of knowledge.

If the world is sometimes slow to recognize the importance of fundamentally new experimental facts, it is not to be wondered at if it is slower still in appreciating and accepting new theoretical ideas. Usually, such new ideas are looked upon with indifference or suspicion, and many years of persistent advocacy and powerful observational support are required before the investigator can hope to see his ideas generally accepted. The story is often told of Arrhenius and the doctorate thesis which he presented to Stockholm University containing his new ideas regarding the nature of solutions, supported by a great volume of experimental data. All that he received for this epoch-making work was a fourth-class degree permanently disqualifying him from an academic career. Arrhenius happily survived this experience, and lived to receive the Nobel Prize and to be venerated as his country's greatest scientist. But there are, unhappily, other instances of youthful genius being repressed and completely suppressed as well.

If there is one fact more than any other which stands out in the history of science, it is the remarkable extent to which great discoveries and youthful genius stand associated together. Scores of instances can be quoted in support of this proposition. Indeed, if one were to attempt to write a treatise on any branch of science in which all discoveries made by youthful workers were left out, there would be very little left to write about. The fact of the matter appears to be that, other things being the same, the principal requisite for success in scientific research is not the maturity of knowledge associated with age and experience, but the freshness of outlook which is the natural attribute of youth. The conservatism which develops with increasing age is thus revealed as a factor which militates against great achievement in science. The great ideas seem to come most easily to youthful minds. Since however much time is required to work out a new idea properly and fully, age and experience are not altogether useless in science. Up to a certain point, the conservatism bred by age may even be useful as a brake on the wilder flights of youthful imagination. Further even the elderly may, if they so choose, retain and cherish a youthful spirit and outlook. So long, therefore, as they do not allow the conservatism of age to function as a suppressor of youthful genius, the elderly may continue to find themselves useful as guides and inspirers of research. On this view, indeed, the principal function of the older generation of scientific men is to discover talent and genius in the younger generation and to provide ample opportunities for its free expression and expansion.

So far I have said little about the nature of the urge which leads the elite few to devote themselves to science and live laborious days in its service. This is a part of the larger question, what is it that drives men to devote themselves to any type of idealistic activity? I think it will be readily conceded that the pursuit of science derives its motive power from what is essentially a creative urge. The painter, the sculptor, the architect and the poet, each in his own way, derives his inspiration from nature and seeks to represent her through his chosen medium, be it paint, or marble, or stone, or just well-chosen words strung together like pearls on a necklace. The man of science is just a student of nature and equally derives his inspiration from her. He builds or paints pictures of her in his mind, through the intangible medium of his thoughts. He seeks to resolve her infinite complexities into a few simple principles or elements of action which he calls the laws of nature. In doing this, the man of science, like the exponents of other forms of art, subjects himself to a rigorous discipline, the rules of which he has laid down for himself and which he calls logic. The pictures of nature which science paints for us have to obey these rules, in other words have to be self-consistent. Intellectual beauty is indeed the highest kind of beauty. Science, in other words, is a fusion of man's aesthetic and intellectual functions devoted to the representation of nature. It is therefore the highest form of creative art.

paints on a surface. The man of science is just a
student of nature, and equally derives his inspiration
from her. He beholds or paints pictures of her in his
mind, through the intangible medium of his thought.
He seeks to resolve her infinite complexities into a few
simple principles or elements of action which he calls
the laws of nature. In doing this, the man of science,
like the exponents of other forms of art, subjects himself to a rigorous discipline, the rules of which he has
laid down for himself, and which he calls logic. The
pictures of nature which science paints for us have to
obey these rules; in other words, have to be self-
consistent. Intellectual beauty is indeed the highest
kind of beauty. Science, in other words, is a fusion of
man's aesthetic and intellectual faculties devoted to
the representation of nature. It is therefore, the highest
form of creative art.

INDEX

INDEX

INDEX

INDEX